In a Devonshire Carrier's Van.

Tales told in the Devon Dialect.

By "JAN STEWER."

Broad Street Publishing

First published in Facsimile in 2012 by
BROAD STREET PUBLISHING

ISBN: 978-0-9557019-9-3

Printed and bound in Great Britain by
Short Run Press Limited, Exeter

BROAD STREET PUBLISHING
Arden Cottage, Coombeshead Road, Highweek
Newton Abbot TQ12 1PZ
Tel +44 (0) 1626 365478

This facsimile edition of Jan Stewer's In a Devonshire Carrier's V
is published with the kind permission of A J Coles's grand-daught
Mrs Barbara Harrington

+❊ CONTENTS. ❊+

How George Hurford was Bested.

"ROUN' tuther zide Missis Snell," says Tom Zalter, the draiver, "laur bless my 'art; mean to zay yu bin raidin' in my van all thase years, an' pretend yu dunnaw which zide the stap be to. Now idn' that jis' like a wumman, Jan?" 'e says to me, "to go plattin' all roun' there in the mud an' slush 'stead o' gettin' up yer close to the path."

"Git 'ome," er says, "I be in a 'urry to git up out o' the rain. I shall be wat right in droo in a minit."

"Wull, yu ant improved matters trapesin' all aroun' the van like that, onless yu be doin' o't vir the benevit o' yer health. Come on, do 'e; vokes 'ull think yu'm a zircus trollopin roun' an' roun' like that."

Missis Snell 'ad walked all aroun' th' osses' haids to the wrong zide, an' now 'er waint all aroun' the back o' the van to where 'er started vrom.

"Gi's yer 'and, Missis," says Tom, "an' let's be auf, else us waun' git back 'ome avore the rain staps. Jim, zit back on that 'arf-bag o' tetties, wull 'e? an' let missis zit in your plaace, onless yu'd rather 'ave 'er in yer lap. But I shidn' advise 'e to, vir I swear 'er's a stone heavier than 'er was las' wik. I nivver zeed anybody improve like yu du, missis."

3

"Yume turrable personal, Tom, I sem," says missis, "'tis onpolite to tell a lady 'er's gettin' stout."

"Aw, wull!" says Tom, "I'd rather that than raims o 'joy like Missis Park'ouze is gettin'. 'Er's like a bag o' cloas-pigs. But I daun' caal yume too fat, missis—ony jis' comferable. Wy! who's theas? I be dalled if Peter Davey idn' comin'. Come on, Measter Davey, all the winders in the wordle yu wadn' laived be'ind."

"They tauld me up to th' Elephant yu was gone," says Peter, "but I reckoned I shid ketch 'e, cuz yu mos' times got a vu arrants to pick up on yer way out."

"Lucky vir yu I 'ad," says Tom, "an' aven then I doubt if you'd a-bin in time if 'tadn' a-bin ver missis yer rayquirin' a li'l axercise around the van avore 'er got up. I dunnau wher' yume gwain to sit to, but yu better way squaise in there some-plaace; yule git wat's muck out yer."

"Wat 'bout yu then, Tom?"

"Aw! laur bless 'e, I daun take naw 'count o' the wat. I be got perfidious to't b' theas time."

"Wull, Measter Davey," says Tom agean arter us ad got zettled an' started, "ave 'e bin doin' aught in the poetin' line laately. Us 'ant yeard noan o' your po'try sence that bit yu med out back Kursmas."

"Wull Tom," says Peter, "I got a bit in me pocket now wat I med out bout ole George Hurford. Du yu mind when 'ees wive bested 'n?"

"Ees fai. Shid think I du. Yu ant med out a tale about thik?"

"Wat'll 'e bet?"

" Darn 'ee, git vore'n raid'n then. 'Twull
be weth yerin', I warr'ner."

HOW GEORGE HURFORD WAS
BESTED.

AND BY HIS OWN WIFE AND ALL!

Now, harken to me all gude people I pray;
I'll tull 'e o' zummat wat 'appened wan day,
When Measter George 'Urvord was bested vir
    wance,
Who by, shid 'e think? Wy, 'ees awn gude
    wife, Nance.

Ole George was a maason, an' gude to 'ees traade,
But the laazies' vagabone ever was maade;
In vac', 'twaz zo long sence 'eed builded a wall
That us purt'near virgot wat 'ees trade was 't al'.

'Twaz orwiz rayported roun' yer an' about,
That Georgie an' Work 'ad a row, an' vaaled out,
But whe'er that be right now, or wrong, I can't
    zay;
They wadn' on no coortin' terms anyway.

Eed worked in 'ees young days—the smuthe wi'
    the rough;
Then 'e zuddenly thought that 'eed worked long
    enuff;
Zo 'e zed 'eed git married, an' choose out a wive
As cude work an' maintain 'en the raist of 'ees
    live.

Zo 'e coorted Nance 'Awkins, an' axed 'er to
    marr',
'Cuz 'e knawed 'er was 'customed to rin, vetch,
    an carr',
Waish an' scrub, wring an' rub, patch an' zew,
    bake an' brew—
An' 'e 'lowed 'er cude get through nuff work vir
    the two.

The maid little knawed wat a live 'er'd be led,
When Georgie wan Zaterday axed 'er to wed.

'Er didn't think twaice, but 'er jumped to the
    chance;
"I mid nivver be ax'd any more," thought Miss
    Nance.

Then George putt away all 'ees tools in the shed,
And 'anged up 'ees trowel to the voot o' the bed,
To look at o' mornens, an' think o' the chaps
Force to go out to work—rainin' cats an' dogs
    praps.

Vir George nivver got up so sune as 'e woke;
'E lied on to raidee the paaper, an' smauk.
A zauf' veather bed zuited George vurry wull.
Aw, yer now! E knaw'd wat was gude vir 'izzul'.

"Tidn' laazy," 'e says. "but tis tired that I veels,
An' I've yeard 'tis onhealthy to work between
    meals;
An' bezides, if a chap's got to work all 'ees live,
Wat the juice is the use of 'ees 'aving a wive?"

Nance zeed twadn't no gude to cry an' to sob,
Zo 'er jis med the best o' a vurry bad job.
'Er man widn work—an' twaz no use to tell;
Zo 'er turn-to an' do'd all the lot be 'erzell.

An' that's jis' the divvurnce tween wumman an'
    man,
If HER'S wrong, HE volleys, so vast as 'e can,
An' blames 'er vir all—but when HUSBAND'S a
    sloth,
The WIFE pins 'er sleeves back an' labours vir
    both.

Nance was up ev'ry mornen vrim vower to 'ar-
    past,
An' er'd bide up so long as 'er poor limbs 'ud
    last;
An' all the wile toilin' like any black slaave.
(An' George grawin' wiskers—too laazy to
    shaave).

Till tain ev'ry mornen 'eed slape like the daid;
'Er carr'd up 'ees lunch where 'e was to in bade;
Or if 'er was gwain off to work vir the day
Er'd lef' zummat 'andy when 'er waint away.

Vir Nance 'ad to work to kape George an' erzell,
By gwain out waishin, an' charrin' as well,
Or taakin in zewin'—er'd stitch 'arf the night,
'Till 'er ayes burned like vire wi' the dull cannle-
    light.

All Mondy an' Tuesdy 'er stude to the tub,
An' Wainsdy 'er waint to the Manor to scrub,
Then 'er worked to the Rect'ry, kep' church clain,
    an' skule—
An' 'anded the money to George like a fule.

An' zame time er'd got all 'er awn work as well,
Vir George widn' stir to do ort vir hissell;
Not aven the gard'n—tiz true, I declare,
Nance tilled ev'ry tettie that ever was there.

'Er spit up the garden an' tilled the 'awl rap,
The banes, pais, an' cabbidges—do'd ev'ry scrap;
Er'v come 'ome nights raddy to drop right away,
An' vorce to dig tetties vir boilin' nex day.

The money which Nance did zarr' tollin' all day
George spaind of a night to the pub 'crass the
    way,
The "Black Oss," where all 'ees old cronies did
    meet—
Bill 'Arris, Jim Webber, Jan Pratt, an' Dick
    Street.

If yu caaled in "Black Oss" any evenin' yu mind,
Roun' the vire thik there party yu mos' sure to
    vind,
Bright spaicimens too; an' nit wan o' the vive
But was spaindin' in beer wat was arned by 'ees
    wive.

Let a man be so laazy as ever yu will,
'Ee's boun' to do zummat to pass the taime still,
If 'e daun veel inclined to do nothin' no gude
'Ee'l get into murchy—an' that's wat George do'd.

Sence 'eed gived up the trowel, the mortar an'
    lime,
'E wanted vir zummat to pass by the time;
'E stidded a gude wile wat 'e could contrive;
Then daycided 'eed start vindin' vault wi' 'ees
    wive.

Arter that poor Nance simmed 'er cude do nothin'
    right,
It was niggin' an' naggin' vrim mornen till night ;
Watever 'er do'd, an' watever 'er zed,
It was sure to be wrong ; till 'er wished 'erzel
    dead.

But still 'er slaved on orwiz doin' 'er best,
Though George nivver gived 'er not wan
    moment's rest ;
But 'er hide up 'er troubles an' jis waint along,
Content wile 'e used nothin' wiss'n ees tongue.

Wan night 'e come 'ome in a shockin bad mood ;
Eed drenked till 'e veeled like a owl wat bin
    stewed—
Poor Nance 'pon ees toe let a vlat-ayter* drap ;
An' 'e gived 'er a leatherin' with 'ees buckle strap.

When George waint up-baid if 'e adn' bin blind,
'Eed a-zeed that eed laived zummat dangerous
    be'ind,
For yu let a wumman git ever so law,
Her'll turn on a man when 'ee'v gived 'er a blaw.

Nex' day was the Revel to Babblecombe Town,
Witch George widn' miss if yu gived'n vi' poun',
Vor he meaned enjoyin' hissell to the feet (fête)
Wi' Bill 'Arris, Jim Webber, Jan Pratt, an' Dick
    Street.

In the morn when 'e aupened ees ayes 'bout o'
    nine,
'E zeed that the weather was lovely an' vine,
Zo 'e rolled on 'ees zide cuz 'e knawed 'e shid
    vind
The lunch wat ees missis laived orwiz be'ind.

There George zeed a butivul PAI—an' the zight
Med ees mouthe an' ees ayes aup'n wide wai'
    delight.
Be the zide was a bit of a noat where twaz zed,—
" I aupes yu'll like theas LIVER PAI witch I've
    med."

" Haw, haw, Liver Pai ! " shouted George in 'ees
    glee,
" The leatherin mus' 'ave improved 'er I zee.

---

* Flatiron.

'Ad I knawed wat effec' 'twid 'ave 'ad, wy, gude
  laur !
I be dalled I'd a gived 'er a hidin' avore."

'E zune 'ad a 'awl in the crist—which was tough,
But 'e didn' mine that cuz the mait was enuff,
Eed zoonder 'ave liver than mutton or pork,
Zo into a nice bit 'e zune sticked 'ees vork.

But tell 'bout the crist ! wat 'bout th' inzide ?
Says George "Mos' like leather that ever I tried ! "
AN LEATHER IT WAS, as 'e zune zeed vull well,
Vir the nex' thing 'e vound was the buckle hissel'.

ER'D MED'N A STRAP-PAI ! George jumped out
  o' baid,
An lat out a yell vit to waaken the daid.
"Yu wait till I'm drassed, I'll zune shaw yu
  aroun' " ;
But sarch where 'e wid, not a thing to be vound !

No burches, no weskit, no coat, an' no zocks.
Bezides that er'd turned all the kays in the locks !
Zo yer was poor Georgie alas ! an' alack !
In prison wi' nort but a shirt to 'ees back.

'E aupened the winder, and olleyed out "Vire ! "
Till all the vokes rinned up the strait to inquire.
Then George told 'ees tale, 'ow 'e cuden git out ;
An' when the vokes yerd it—Mai ! didn 'um shout ?

"Zarve 'e right you ole bagger," the wimmen
  voke zed,
"Bes' thing yu can do is to get back een bed."
"Drap down out a-winder," says wan, "Yu
  won' hurt."
"'Ow can I ?" says George, "wai' nort on but
  me shirt ? "

'E tried to persuade 'em to drow up zom cloas,
But the joke was too gude to spoil, yu mid
  suppose ;
Bill 'Arris, Jim Webber, Jan Pratt, an' Dick Street
Wished Georgie "Gude-bye"—they was off to
  the feet.

There George 'ad to stap till the las' thing o' night,
Wai' nivver a sup, an' wai' nivver a bite ;
An' when Nance come 'ome Georgie promished
  er sure
Eed NIVVER lift 'and to a wumman no more.

Every Man to his Trade.

———•———

" THE bigges' mistaake that any man can
ever make," says Turney Gurney,
" is to think that he id'n sitch a
vule as he looks."

" 'Tis a very common mistaake then,
Turney," says Tom Zalter, the draiver.

" 'Tis the very commones' mistaake of all,"
he says; " but f'r all that there's no greater
mistaake a-maade. Ninety-nine men out of
ev'ry hunderd is a darn sight bigger vules
than they looks. An' so's the tuther wan,
aunly he knaw'th it, an' therevore he id'n
'ardly so likely to shaw it. 'Tis them as is
vules an' daun' knaw it that gi's theirzel's
away so much."

" Yu spaik f'r yerzel Mester Gurney," says
Mis's Endycott.

" Bless yer 'art, missis," says Tom, " so 'e
is spaikin' f'r he's-sel'. He've got zummat
'p'n he's mind he wants to tell about. Let's
have it, Turney. Be yu gwain to get out to
Dicks's Lane Mis's Carpenter?"

" Nit to-day, Tom. If Mester Gurney's
gwain to tell up wan of he's aul' crams I'll
raide on to Vower Crasses, an' go down droo
Orcombe Bottom."

" Ther's a compliment vor 'e Turney,"
says Tom. " Yu ought to be abble to tell us
a yarn arter that."

" I dunnow as I got aught to tell 'e," says
Turney. " I was aunly thenkin' wat vules
men du make o' ther'zels z'mtaimes."

"Aw, wull," says Tom, "let's yer the pa'ticler time you'm thenkin' o'; when you med a vule o' YOUR zelf."

*   *   *   *   *   *   *

Ther's wan gurt vailin in most all men, says Turney, which causes a dale o' trouble z'mtaimes, an' that is the belief that if they was in zumbody else's shoes they cude manage better'n wat that person du hissel'. Daun matter whu he is or wat he is. A varmer 'ull tull 'e that if he cuden make a better passen than wat Mester Zo-an-zo du, he'd nivver praich a zarmint no more. An' in zac'ly the zame way the passen 'ull declare that if he was a varmer he'd lick all the varmers in the parish. The tailor thinks he cude taiche better'n wat skulemaister du, an' skulemaister reckons he cude make better boots than the cobbler.

And ev'ry man thinks that ev'ry other man's way o' gettin' he's livin' is aisier than he's awn. They virgits 'tis aunly the chap wat's wearin' the shoe c'n tell where 'e pinches to.

"Wat an aisy life a varmer's is," says the clurk at he's desk. "Orwiz out in the aup'n air, aunly got to walk along be'ind a plough, or zit up in a trap an' draive into market."

An' the varmer zays, "I wish I was a clurk to be orwiz in out o' the wet an' cauld, wi' nort to du but bite off the tap of a pen, an' scratch in a vew viggurs into a buke."

An' zo it go'th on, ev'rybody thinkin he id'n 'aaf sitch a vule as vokes takes 'n to be.

Wull, yu cuden expec' me to be no divvurnt from the rest, cude 'e ? An' zo, when I went into my brither-law's to stap vir a bit

of a ollerdy wan taime, I zoon beginned to
tell up the zame zort o' tale.

My brither-law was my wive's brither—
Staddon he was caaled, an' he kep' a sort of
a grocer's shop in town. Doin' very well he
was, too, an' is now I bleeve. But I purt'
near stapped all he's custom wan day begad.

'Twas like this yer. As I zed jis now, me
an' my wive went to stap long o' they vir a
vortnit jis f'r a bit of a change like. Wull,
o' coose Ned cuden laive the plaace a great
deal durin' the day-time, so I was in an' out
the shop most o' the taime watchin' he zarr'
the customers, an' lis'nin to the peculiar
things zome o'm did ax vor.

So I zune got to knaw where mos' the
things was kep to; an' p'n-taimes I'd 'and 'en
acrass any li'l thing if I was handiest to 'n.

"Us'll zune maake a grocer of 'e Peter,"
he'd zay to me z'm-taimes, jist by way of a
joke like.

"Ees," I use to think to mezel, "an' if I
ban't so turrable mistaken I shid make a
darn zight better grocer than wat you du
now." Cuz I use to sem he was most
doosted slaw like z'm-taimes, an' kip vokes
waitin while he was vidlin about weighin up
zummat or nuther, when I vancied I cude
a-zar'd two vokes in the taime.

I auf'n use to zay to my wive when us
was aloan, "My days, wat a aisy time o't a
shopkeeper 'ave got compeered wi' a varmer.
Orwiz indoors an' nort to du but weigh up a
vew passels o' tay an' shugger, or hat off a
bit o' baacon, an' zo vooth. An' the money
commin in like a rinnin' strame o' watter.
I wish I'd bin brought up to be a grocer," I
says.

Wull, very vunny thing, twad'n but a day or two arterwads that I 'ad a chance to try me 'and to it—an' I dawn want to be a grocer no more; I zooner go crackin' stones.

It ap'm'd like this yer. I was stood in the shop wan day tellin' to Ned 'bout wan thing an' tuther, an' ther' ad'n bin a zaul in the shop vir zome taime, zo bim-by he says to me:

"Peter," he says, "ther' dawn zem to be nobody about s'mornen, so I'll jis taake the oppertunity an' flip aroun' the cornder to git a shaave an' ha' me 'air cut. They'm orwiz zo vull up nights. Eef anybody shid 'ap'm in, jis gi' the missis a caal; her'll come down an' zarve 'em."

"Or-right, Ned, aul' man," I zes, "that'll be or-right," an' zo, with the zame, out he goes.

'Pon me zaul, he was 'ardly gone out to the door avore in comes a customer. 'Twas a li'l maid. I did'n caal up to Mis's Staddon, cuz I reckoned I cude zar' be'ind the counter so well as uther-wan o'm.

"Wat f'r yu my li'l maid?" I says, lainin' out auver the counter.

"Plaise f'r a tin o' coco," her says, and putts down a zixp'nce.

I raiched down a teen and wrap min up in a bit o' paaper. Twad'n the naites' passel ever was, but I reckoned I shid zoon improve wi' a bit o' practice. I putt the zixp'nce in the teel, an' her waint off. Her'd no zoonder gone than in come a boy f'r a pennerd a sweets. I'd zeed Ned do up a pennerd of sweets in wan of thase yer bags yu makes around yer hand, wat goes down to a point down bottom. I'd nivver tried to make wan avore, but it looked aisy 'nuff, zo I tooked up a bit o' paaper an' started twiddlin' o't around. But I cuden maake 'n go right no-ow. I tried a frash bit o' paaper arter the fus' bit was craised all up, an' I tried 'n fus' wan way an' then tuther, but twad'n a bit o' gude.

An' while I was strugglin' wai' this yer blassid bag dree more com' in—two wimmen an' a boye. I knaw'd they was laafin to zee me tryin' to maake a bag, so I was fo'ce to gi' it up to last, an' screw up the sweets in a bit o' paaper.

Then I went to 'tend to the wimmen. They both beginned to name their arrants to wance, an' both aw'm wanted 'bout a dizzen divvurnt things; an' they wid'n wait f'r me to vetch 'em wan to a taime, nuther.

" Tay—zaup—cannles—butter—cloas-pigs —" they was rattlin' 'em off like wan-a-clock.

" Yer, stiddy on," I says. " Wat do 'e taake me vor, a blessed member o' parly-ment ? Wan to a taime. What do you want missis ? "

" Arf-a-pound o' eighteenpenny tay," her says.

I did'n knaw which was the eighteenpenny tay, but I reckoned it did'n make much odds, so I tooked it out o' the fus' tin I come to. Ned zed arterwads twuz aaf-crown tay I let the wumman ha', but he sure to zay that. I got vore purty wull wi' the tay till it come to wrappin' o't up, an' then I cuden get the ainds to bide in. So to last I was fo'ce to putt it into a biskit bag.

B' thees time I was swattin' purty middlin', an' wishin' Ned 'ud come back. The shop wis 'aaf full o' people, but I was determin'd to let 'em zee I knawed wat I was about.

" Nex' thing plaize ? " I says, jis like a rale shopman.

" Aaf-pound o' vat baacon," her says. So I hat off wat I reckoned was 'bout 'aaf-pound, an' putt'n in the weights. Laur, he went down wi' a bump. I putt two or dree more weights in tuther zide, but did'n lift it.

" I said 'aaf-pound," her says, " nit aaf-hunderdweight." So I cut the piece in aaf, an' wrapped up wan bit in paaper. 'Twas more'n aaf-pound a gudish bit, but I caaled it aaf-pound, cuz I wid'n knaw wat to charge else. B'thees time the tuther vokes in shop was wantin' to knaw whe'er they was gwain to be 'tended to thees wik or nex'. An' wan woman tooked up her basket an' went out agean. I caaled to her that I'd tend to her next, and her zed, " Or-right, then I'll caal around agean the latter part of the week."

The boye keeped on worritin f'r a pound o' traicle. Zo I thort I'd get rid of he fust. Zo I tooked he's jar an' putt'n in under the traicle barreel. But 'twas slaw work rinnin' out; zo I thought I'd tend to zomebody else while 'twaz comin. Jis' then in comes the li'l maid wot I zarr'd fust.

" Please mother zes can't yu tull the divvernce 'tween coco an' musterd, an' yu nivver let me ha' no change."

I tooked back the musterd an' let her ha' a tin o' coco.

" Did'n I let 'e ha' no change, me dear ? " I says.

" No," her says, " an' mother says it ought to be vowerpence hap'my."

So I gi'd her the vowerpence hap'my, an direc'ly her'd gone I railized that wat her mother mained was that the coco was vowerpence hap'my, not the change. But I cuden rin arter 'er, there was so many aroun' me.

"'Ave 'e got very much traicle in thikky bareel, mister?" says the boye.

"Plenty 'nuff f'r yu," I says.

"Aw, I did'n knaw," he says. "Aunly, if yu dawn' turn 'en off middlin' zoon us'll all ha' to get outzide or swim vor't."

Aw, my days! I rished auver to the bareel; but long 'vore I got there me veet got sticked to the vloor. There was a prapper lake o' traicle, an' ev'rywhere I went I laived traicle tracks be'ind me.

Jis' then in comes Ned, an' wat he did zay I muzzen tell 'e.

But wat I zed was, "Ev'ry man to he's trade, an' nivver think yu knaws more about another man's bizness than wat he du hissel'."

Abram's Dog Licence.

———

"WAS that ole Abram Selley you was telling to in Market s'mornen, Tom?"

"Ees, twas Abram right 'nuff; an' a nice purty boye he es, too."

"He was orwiz a dry ole stick," I says, "but as gude-arted a fella as ever drayed breath. I see'd yu was laafin' purty middlin' auver summat. I spaus Abram have bin up to some of he's aul' itums down where he's livin' to now, same's he use to when he was up yer about."

"Ees," says Tom, "he ab'm improved very much, daun' sim so; or, if he have, 'tis for the wiss. He was tellin' me up wan li'l bit of a shanty he had wi' the policeman in the parish where he's living to now.

"Seems this-yer policeman is wan o' they bumtious, high-stappin' soort, summat like thik young fella they 'ad auver to Barley-combe a year or two agone; he wat got Varmer Hurvord fined vorty shillins f'r 'lowing he's cattle to stray p'n the highway. Cou'se yu knaws wat the vokes said 'bout thikky caase. They reckoned the policeman zeed ole Varmer's geat was un-apsed, an' he heed away around the cornder for two howers waitin' f'r the cattle to stray out p'n the rawd; an' soon's the fus' wan putt he's nawse outzide the geat away goes Mister Policeman an' taakes out a summons agin varmer.

17   c

" Wull, this yer chap wat Abram Selley was tellin about was summat similer b' all accounts. An' Abram managed to 'front 'en a'most drec'ly arter he got down there. I dunnaw wat 'twas 'bout zac'ly, but I spaus Abram was makin' he's li'l jokes as usual, an' policeman he did'n 'preciate it altogether. Be-as-twul, he got the idaya that Abram was makin' spoort o'n, an' tryin' f'r to maake 'en look vulish, an' zo he tooked a dislike to 'en, an' ever arterwards he do'd he's uttermos' to try an' ketch 'en in zome li'l thing or nuther so's he cude bring 'en up avore he's betters.

" Well, Abram did'n altogether like the way this-yer bobby was orwis tracking o'n about, an' volleyin ev'rywhere he went to zee if 'e cude capture 'en the wiss f'r liquor, or in anything he no bizness doin' o'. An' to-last Abram took to insultin' o'n out in aup'n bevore other vokes, which natterally aunly med things wiss.

" Owsumever, wan day Abram was into the village pub wi' wan or two, an' he be-ginned tellin' up 'bout this-yer policeman, wat he sh'd do, an' wat he shid'n do, an' wat he shid say, an' so foorth.

" ' He thinks he'm turrable smart,' says Abram, ' watchin' me right an' lef', up hill an' down. An' THEN he can't vind nort up agin me ; but I be aunly laafin' o'n all the while. He thinks he'm sharp, but he's blind's a bat. If he wad'n he cude zee zum-mat wat never ought to be. Right under he's very nawse, aunly he can't zee't. He'm too big a vule.'

" Now, policeman were outzide the door all the time Abram was tellin', heark'nin to wat he'd got to zay.

" 'Wat is it hĕ ab'm zeed then, Mester Zelley ? ' says wan chap.

" 'Wy,' says Abram, ' I be keepin' vower dogs f'r wan thing, now this very minnit, an' workin' two o'm EV'RY day. An' I ab'm got a lishence f'r nuther wan o'm.'

" ' But you'm 'lowed a certain number wai'out a lishence,' says another chap, ' 'cordin to the quantity o' sheap yu got.'

" ' Wan, I be 'lowed,' says Abram, ' but I ban't countin' he 't'al'. I keeps vive if I counts he.'

" Jis' then in walks policeman, an' I spaus the vaces o' the chaps in the bar was a picter. Abram tried to flip out droo the door, but the bobby stap' 'en.

" ' 'Arf a minnit, Mester Zelley,' he says. ' I jis' wants to inform yu that I shall charge yu wai' keeping dugs wai'out uther lishence. An' yu, an' yu, an' yu (spaikin' to the chaps stood around), I shall want yu f'r witnesses to wat you've yerd Maister Zelley say by he's awn confession aunly a minnit or two agone.'

" Wull, sure 'nuff, Abram got a bit o' blue paaper a day or two arterwads, an' he was fo'ced to go bevore he's betters.

" ' Abram Zelley,' the magistrate says to 'en, ' you'm charged wai' keepin' on sitch-n-sitch a daate vower dugs wai'out takin' out a lishence. Wat 'ave yu to zay to't. Be yu guilty or not guilty ? '

" ' Wull, yer 'onner,' says Abram, ' I be, an' I ban't, if yu understan'.

" ' But I daun' understan',' says the jidge —or magistrate, I should say—getting into a tantrum. ' Wat do yu mane by yu BE an' yu BAN'T ? 'Ow can yu BE if yu BAN'T ; or 'ow can yu BAN'T if yu BE ? '

"'Wull, yer 'onner,' says Abram, "'tis like as this. I want deny but wat I'd a-got the vower dugs on the date in question——'

"'An' did yu 'ave a lishence vor'm?' says old eagle-eye.

"'No, yer 'onner, I did'n.'

"'Wull, then, an wy did'n yu?'

"'Wull, yer worship, 'tis like as this. Two o'm was cloamen dugs, an' was zot up tap o' the mantleshelf; an' tuther two was the vire-dugs down p'n the 'arth. So I raly did'n think there was any caal f'm me to go to the expense of a lishence.'

"Aw, my blessid! 'Cordin' to wat Abram told me, thikky there court was in a prapper uproar. Cou'se, the room was vulled up wai varmers, an' if they did'n laaf—wull, yu knaws wat a Deb'nsher varmer's laaf is like when he gits a prapper start. The magistrate he raved, an' swore, an' teared he's 'air, an' the policeman tried to chow the nub off the tap of he's helmit.

"All of a sudden they zeed that the bobby was tryin' f'r to spaik; so arter a while they managed to get the vokes a bit quiet.

"'Did'n yu say bevore witnesses,' says the policeman, 'that yu was workin' two o' the dugs ev'ry day?'

"'Ees,' says Abram, 'I bleeve I did. An' 'twas Gospel truth, too. They was the vire dugs. An' I tell 'e wat 'tis, this caul' weather they daun' get a minnit's rest nuther. Wy, 'tis wan body's work to carr' in the 'ood to keep 'em to work.'

"That zot 'em all off ageun, an' the magis-trate dismissed the caase quick's he cude. But twad'n very many days afterwards avore Mester Policeman was shifted off to another pareesh."

Reuben Ley in the Higher Circle.

PART I.

REUBEN LEY was sot back in the back part o' the van. He was so quiet us didn' 'ardly nawtice 'en fir a bit—dimpsey and all.

"Ullaw Reuben," says Tom Zalter, the draiver, "I sem you'm turrable quiet back there in the cornder. Wat be stiddin'—nex' year's a'manac?"

Reuben 'ab'm rawd in the van since I dunnaw when. In fac', I dawn b'leeve, unless I'm very much mistaken, that I've ever mentioned he's naame to 'e so much. Tidn very auf'n folks up bout Broadmead goes into Exeter. 'Tis mos'ly Barnstable or Zouthmolton wi' they. An' if they DO 'tis almost so well for'm to cut acrass to Excombe Station as wat tiz to trapes all the way to Muddlecombe, an' raide in the van.

When Rueben use to live auver yer to Wick us use to zee 'en very auf'n. Either he or he's missis use to raide into Exeter EV'RY wik wi' the butter 'n heggs 'n poultry, fir they was dairy varmers to start wai'; an' then they graj'ly got on, wan thing to another, and increased and increased and alwiz sem to have the best o' luck, an' now they'm livin' raytired like gen'lvokes, in a butivul houze, wai' man-sarvants an' maid-sarvants, and

21

hoxes and hasses, an' I dunnaw what-all bezides.

But Reuben he dawn' care fir that zort o' life. Tidn' suiting he 't all. He's wan o' the gude ole rough-'n-raddy, Joan-blunt zort, Reuben is. Burches and leggins is he's style, an' a bit of a handkercher around he's neck; and he likes he's pipevul o' black-jack an' he's quart of zider. But tiz he's missis an' darter that do's it all. They'm prapperly maazed 'bout havin' ev'rything viddy, an' actin' like the gen'lvokes. They 'ant got but the wan cheel, an' her was zend away to a boardin' skule up about Bristol someplaace fir two or dree years to be finished off. And I be darned if her wad'n finished off now, prapper. When her went away her was jis like any poor body's cheel, an' spoke so broad, jis like my maid or any o' the rest.

But my jaly! When her come back you wid'n a-knawed her fir the same maid. Reuben had left Wick by that time, an' tooked a big farm somewhere out Kirton way. But Missis Ley and Miss Marian, as they calls her now, comed out wan day to pay us a visit. Her name orwiz use to be Mary Ann afore her went to boarding skule, an' they use to call her Poll, but now tiz Miss Marian, begad! And I shid a-past her vifty times an' never knawed her fir the same. Her was drassed like a princess an' her walked like a quane, an' when her talked, it prapperly med the swattin come out all auver 'e, her sim to be workin' so hard. And the mother! Laur bless my 'art! You'd a'swared her was nothin' less'n a duchess. An' when HER tried to spaik like the grand vokes twas wiss'n the maid. Purt' near made the valse teeth jump out of her haid.

"'Tis gude to be some vokes," says Tom to Reuben, "Nort to du, and livin' on the vat o' the land."

"Tiz gude to be them vokes wat knaws when they'm well off," says Reuben. "If I'd knawed when I was well off I'd never have gived up business."

"Wat did 'e for then?" says Tom.

"Same's a gude many fules else, Tom," he says. "To plaise the wimmen voke. Time was when my wive 'ud milkee an' make butter, an' boil pig's-mate, an' zook the calves, an' take the things to market—and got to begad. But now, caw bless my zaul, I'm expectin ev'ry day when her's gwain to ring the bell fir a sarvant maid to come and wipe her nawse."

"I wish I cude be a lady, an' nit 'ave to work 'ard fir me living," says Mis' Snell.

"Daunee zay that, missis," says Reuben. "If that's wat yu caals bein' a lady, same's my missis is now, I be darned if 'tidn' a sight harder work than keepin' a dairy."

"Rummage," says Mis' Snell, "a lady c'n do jis wat her's mind to."

"Aw! can 'er?" he says. "That's where yu makes the bigges' mistake o' YOUR lifetime. Mind, I daun' say but wat it mid be or-right fir they wat bin orwiz born an' brought up to it. But when 'tiz a thing yu 'ant bin 'customed to, an' yu comes to try to start it all to wance like, wai'out any practice, as the saying is, wy, I tells 'e tiz 'ard work—doosted 'ard work."

"Blest if I c'n make that out, c'n you Mis' Endycott?" says Mis' Snell. "If you'm a

lady an' got a-plenty of money to buy wat,
you mind, and do what you like, I can't zee
where th' 'ard work comes in to."

"Look at yer, Missis," says Reuben.
"Now, I'll jis explain a thing or two to you,
an' then you c'n jidge fir yerzell. When us
lef' Wick, as you du know, us waint into a
varm, smarl wan vust, an' arter a bit us
tooked a bigger wan. Wull, us do'd very
wull; I ban't gwain to deny but wat us do'd
VERY wull, droo the manes of hard work an'
careful management; till bim-by us daycided
us 'ud give up work an' live a vew years in
paice no' quietness, till the lease of our
tenancy of thase yer pore ole bodies of clay
expired. At laist, that's wat I thought us
intended doin' mind. But the wimmen-voke
ad'n got no-jis notions, seems-so. 'Twas the
maid was the ins'igation of it in the fus'
plaace. Her'd a-bin to thase yer high-class
skule 'long of her betters, an' there her'd
picked up wai' some purty ole fantastical
notions I c'n 'sure 'e.

"Cost me a purty penny, thiky there skule
did, an' a middlin' choice lot of old witpot
they larned the maid, too. That was the
fus' thing I ax'd the maid when her come
'ome fir her ollerdys—but I virgot, tidn'
'ollerdys' now, 'tis 'vacations.' They 'aves
'vacations' now-a-days, they daun' 'ave no
ollerdys.

"'Wull, Poll,' I zes, 'what 'ave um larned
'e to skule?'

"'Yu muzzen caal me Poll, 'vather,' her
says,'the t'other girls to skule says 'tiz vulgar.'

"'Aw! fath,' I says, 'wat do 'um caal 'e,
then, when they wants 'e, or do 'um wissle
for 'e?'

" 'Guv'ness caals me Marian,' her says, 'an' that's wat you mus' caal me. 'Tis more polite.'

" 'Laur bless the cheel,' I says, 'I shan' be abble to mind it. But you never didn' use to like bein' caaled Mary Ann.'

" 'Naw-naw,' her says, dappin her vingers to her yers as though her cuden a-bear to yer the zound o't, 'MARIAN,' her says, 'nit MARY ANN. I sh'll have a fit if yu caals me be that name.'

" 'Aw,' I says, 'is Mary Ann vulger too ?'

" 'I shid think it WAS vulger,' her says, 'vulger as dirt.'

" 'Aw, wull,' I says, 'dirt's a very useful article if it's GUDE dirt, an' got plenty of it, an' a vew bushels o' gude zeed to till in it.'

" 'An' I ban't gwain to caal yu " vather " fir the future,' her says, 'I be gwain to caal 'e ' PA ' like all tuther girls to skule.'

" 'Aw, be 'e ?' I says, 'let me ketch 'e ' pa-ing ' me—sitch ole rummidge ; watever next I winder. Is this wat they bin fullin' up yer haid wi' to skule ? Have 'um taiched 'e the way to boil a tettie I winder, or cook a blawter ?'

" 'Aw, PA,' her says, 'vancy cookin' sitch a common thing as a blawter !'

" 'Wul,' thinks I to mezell, 'if things 'av'n come to a purty vine pass I'm blawed.' But laur bless yer 'art soce. That was aunly the beginnin' o't. The maid use to tell auver all thees-yer ole no-sense to her mother, an' they use to rade they ole novel books all about dukes an' laurds, 'n' carriage an' pairs, an' vootmen an' coochmen an' parks an' mansions an' I dunnaw wat-all, till they got ther' haid's vulled up to bustin'

wai't. Then when the maid went back to
skule agean her was invited to wan or two o'
thees-yer grand vine 'ouzes to spaind the
ollerdys—or vacations I SHID zay. Then
ther' was a purty vine ole rumpus drec'ly.
'Marian have bin invited to thayse-yer
places,' says her mother, 'an' it stan's to
raison us'll have to invite they other maidens
back agean.'

"Her'd got the name off pat 'nuff, but
darned if I cude mind it fir ever so long, an'
whenever I zed POLL you'd a-thort I'd med
use of a bad word to zee the grimaces they
did make up.

"Wull, my wive reckoned that us was
now gwain to move in wat her caaled a
higher circle. I spaus they caals it a circle,
'cuz the vokes daun' keep so straight as wat
poor vokes du.

"Be-as-twull, 'fore I knawed where I was
to, 'ardly, us 'ad choozed a houze an' spaind
nuff money to stock a dizzen varms."

"There's wan thing, maister," I says:
"You got a mos' butival houze."

"I daun zay nort about that Jan," he
says. "The plaace is butivul nuff, no doubt.
A zight too butivul to plaise me, I c'n sure
'e. But wat's the gude o't all? 'Tis too
much ole sarrymony fir me. 'Tis like gwain
to skule all auver agean, to larn sich ole
gytes an' itums. They drasses me up like a
monkey-on-a-stick, an' makes me be'ave
like a dancin' bear. I be all out o' plaace
like a cow in a church."

PART II.

THE GARDEN PARTY.

PRELIMINARIES.

Reuben Ley went on,

"Wull, as I said las' wik, they ole invitations was all settled to last. An' mortle plaised wi' therzel's was my wive an' the maid to think wat a gude job they'd made o't.

"'Waun' Mis's Tolley be furious,' says Poll (or Marion I shude say), 'when her fines her ab'm bin axed. But us ab'm got no common vokes 't al,' have us, mother?'

"'Naw, dear,' says her mother, lookin' down auver the list, 'tiz the mos' seleck party ever bin knawed yer-abouts. I bet Mis's Lane 'ull be green wi' jellisness.'

"Wull, yu mid depaind 'pon it, I was prapperly draidin' this yer ole function. Cuz noan o' my ole 'quaintances wad'n axed. They was all too vulger. I was for invitin' Tom Quant an' he's missis, an' Jack Clattery, an' ole Jesse Callaway, and Mis's Callaway an' Jim Partridge, an' the raist o' the big varmers about. Then us 'ud a-had a middlin' gude ole spree, an' finished up wi' a hand to nap. But laur, the wimmen voke wid'n yer it mentioned even.

"'Fancy,' they said. 'Tom Quant to a garden party! He'd come in he's burches an' liggins an' tell 'bout the price o' pork all the time.'

"'Wull,' I says. 'Fancy ME to a garden party then. 'Ow 'bout that? I'd a sight sooner tell about pigs to men like Tom an'

Jack than bide tellin' a lot of ole witpot wi'
a passel o' monkeys like some o' they yu got
down p'n thiky paaper.'

" ' There goes yer vather agean,' says the
missis. ' Can't rise he's mind above the
common level. But daunee take no nawtis
o'n, my dear cheel.'

" ' Ullaw ! ' thinks I to mezel. ' Us be
gettin more like the higher circle ev'ry day—
tellin the cheel nit to take no nawtis of her
awn vather.'

" Owsumever, the invitations wiz got
ready an' zend away b' poast. Prapper
printed cards they was ; they went into
Barnstable same purpose an' 'ad 'em printed.
Twas putt down in wan o' the missis's hatticrat books wat wordin' ought to be putt p'n
the cards. An' when they come back all
printed wi' our name p'n tap o'm, an' invitin
So-an-so to a Garden Party to Broadmead
p'n sitch-an-sitch a date, the missis an' the
maid was like a pair o' chillern wi' a noo
toy. An' I mus' say they looked vurry wull,
c'nsiderin. Missis carr'd wan down to Jane,
the cook-'ousemaid or watever her's caaled.
Jane reckoned twas lovely—' jis like dooks
an' members o' Parlyment do's it,' her said.
An' the missis rised her wages vive pound a
year fir sayin' it.

" Wull, havin' invited the vokes, the nex'
thing to settle was wat they was gwain to
'ave to ait arter they'd come, an' wat they
was to do wi' therzel's while they was there.

" 'Cou'se, so var as the aitin part wis con-
cerned I wad'n axed to 'ave no say in the
matter—seps payin' vor't. But of all the
concoctions ever yu yerd tell about, they
was the most concoctious. 'Cou'se, they

had all ther' idayes out from the hatticrat
books, but the 'moosing part o't was, 'most
all the names o' the divvernt aitables was
wraut in this-yer Vrench langwidge. Wull,
o' cou'se, Poll (or Marion I spaus I ought to
say) her'd larned to spaik Vrench to Boardin'
Skule—an' if yu cude aunly a-yerd she
tryin' f'r to taich her mother the c'rect pronounciation o' they words yu'de a bust yerzel
wi' laafin. I use to say s'metimes, ' Wy
you'm makin' the cat laaf. I c'n zee he's
zides shaakin.'

" Poor ole dumman, her did work mos'
jewsive 'ard to master they jawbreakers, an'
I tull 'e str'ight 'twas purt-near the manes o'
puttin' the big hat on th' aul thing. For
her got that downcouraged 'cuz her cuden
pernounce the things right that her was two
or dree times p'n the point o' jackin it up
altogether.

" Auver 'n auver agean her'd practyse it,
pertendin her was tellin' to somebody in
reality.

" ' Missis Brown,' her'd say, ' won't you
have a li'l bong—bung—bing—no, chong—
ching—stap-a-minit, Marion, I sh'll get it in
a second ' (an' the swattin wid rin down
auver her vaace in strames) ' hote—hope—
hoke—stap-a-minit—'

" ' That's it,' I'd zay, ' hokey-pokey yu
mean.'

" ' —Stap-a-minit,' her'd go agean, ' wong
—pong—stap-a-minit—'

" ' Yer,' I said. ' Mis's Brown 'ull be gone
past it avore her gets aught to ait.'

" ' Be quiet; vather,' says the maid.
' Leave mother aloan. Her'll think o't
bim-by.'

" ' Ees,' I said, ' an' b' that time Mis's
Brown mid be daid o' starvation, an' then
yer mother 'd be summonsed up avore the
jidge f'r wumman-slaughter. Wy daun' 'e
ha' squab-pie or vried baacon 'n 'tetties. Yu
waun' want no Vrench names f'r that, an'
yu cuden ha' nothin' nicer.'

"Owsumever, I spaus th' aul lady manidged
to get around it a bit to last, cuz they 'ad
aul thase yer funny aitables. But I zeed
wan or two o' the laadies smilin' to wan
tuther when her 'axed 'em to ha' some o't;
an' it come into me mind 'bout the li'l tale I
yerd when I went to Dame's skule vifty year
agone—where the jackdaw picked up a vew
paycock's veathers an' sticked min in
amongs' he's awn and tried to pass he's-sel'
off f'r a paycock. An' tuther jackdaws peck
'n all to paices. An' I sem tiz purty much
the zaame wai' jackasses as 'twas wai' jackdaws.

" In fac, Mis's Lane, her gi'd my wive a
turrable scat sure 'nuff. 'Cou'se her was
aunly lookin' vir the oppertunity. So when
missis axed her if her wid'n ha' some ole
trade or nuther (which her tried to caal b'
the Vrench naame) Mis's Lane pertended
her did'n knaw wat her mained.

" ' I daun' think I ever tasted it,' her says.
' I shid like to try it an' zee wat 'tiz like.'

" So yu c'n depaind my missis was proud's
a louse to think her'd got zummat wat Mis's
Lane ad'n nivver tasted (an' ther' was a
host of other ladies stood by), so her marched
off to the taable an' carr'd vore a plaate vul
an' a spoon.

" ' Aw,' says Mis's Lane when her zee'd it.
' Yu main so-an-so (caalin' o't by its propper

pronounciation). Aw, 'ees, I be very fond
o't ; us auf'n haves it. But I did'n knaw yu
mained that when yu axed me to have
some.'

"But I've got ahaid a' me story.

"They zay anticipation's better'n railiza-
tion, an' 'twas in thees caase. 'Twas aisy
nuff makin' out a butivul long list of all the
vokes they'd like to zee to the party—but
'twas a divvern't thing altogether gettin' 'em
there. F'r 'bout of a wik arter they cards
'ad bin zend out thur' wad'n 'ardly a day
passed but wat the paus'man carr'd up two
or dree letters from vokes wat 'ad bin invited,
to zay they was vexed they cuden come.
'Twas a mos' coorious thing wat a host o'm
'ad got ingagements on that very day.

"'I sh'd think us must a-vixed p'n the
very wistest day in th' 'aul year,' says the
maid. An' her was purt near p'n cryin'
when the paus'man let her 'ave anuther arf-
dizzen letters, an' they was all axcuses to
zay 'ow vexed they was they cuden have the
pleasure of comin'. Lais yer knaw, all o't
Nothin' but lais. Cuz I daun' b'leeve f'r
wan instant that they'd all got ingagements
p'n thiky day. Or if they 'ad they made 'em
same purpose so's they shid 'ave a axcuse to
bide away.

"Owsumever, arter that ther' was jis' p'n
vowerty vokes wat wraut an' accepted the
invitation.

"'An' wat you'm gwain to do wi' that
lot,' I says, ' passes my comprehension com-
plately. Be um gwain to walk around wi'
ther' vingers sticked in their mouths all the
time, or zit an' lookee to wan tuther ? '

"'Us 'ave arranged all that,' they says.

' Yu nid'n worrit yerzel. Us be gwain to ha'
lorn-tennis an' croky.'

" ' Where to ? ' I says.

" ' Why, p'n the lawn, 'cou'se,' says the
missis.

" ' Ow can 'e ? ' I says. ' You'm fo'ced to
have ev'rythin' arranged prapper fir that,
'cuz I've zeed 'em playin' about divvernt
plaaces.'

" ' Aw, wull,' her says, ' us got a man
commin' out 'vrim Barnstable spesh'ly to
mark out the lines prapper.'

" ' But daun'ee have to ha' balls an' bats
an' things, an' a net ? Id'n that lorn-tennis
where they haves a net stretched right
acrass ? '

" ' Us 'ave got all that's rayquired now,'
her says. ' So yu nid'n be feared. Us 'ave
ordered all that's necessary.'

" An' I be jiggered if they ad'n, too! I
got a bill a wik or two arterwards vir 'bout
vive-'n-twainty pounds vir lorn-tennis things
and croky things an' all sitch ole rummidge
as that is.

" ' I did'n think it wid be 'ardly so much,'
says my wive. ' But there ! 'tis a thing yu
daun' want to buy ev'ry wik.'

" ' Darn gude job too,' I says, ' else I'm
blawed if us wid'n soon want to shift to the
big-ouze ! ' "

PART III.

THE GARDEN PARTY.

HOW REUBEN PLAYED LAWN TENNIS.

" WULL, Jan, an' Tom, an' the raist of 'e,"

Reuben went on, " the girt day come to-las,'
an' us 'ad thees yer windervul garden party.
An' a purty vine ole shanty twas, too.

" Twid a bin orright, I derzay, if they'd
managed it ther'zels, an' let ev'rybody du
wat they was mind to ; but nort wid'n plaise
'em but I mus' join in, an' make wise I
knowed all about ther' ole lorn-tennis an'
croky, an' all the rest o' the no-sense ole
amoosements they'd got there.

" Vust of all I zed I wid'n ha' nort to du
wai't.

" ' 'Tiz YOUR consarn,' I says, ' an' yu
mus' carr't out as best yu can. I shan
'ave nort to du wai't.'

" Aw, wull then, they was mos' turrable
upzot about theas. Missis her zed I do'd
ev'rything I cude to fustrate their plans an'
keep 'em from risin' long o' the bettermos'
folk. An' the maid her beginned to cry an'
zed they cuden carr't out prapper if I did'n
go out an' tell to the gestis, an' jine in the
games an' sitch like an' zo foorth. So to-las',
f'r paice an' quietness saake, I promised
I'd zee wat I cude do towards it, an' they
undertook to larn me all I'd got to do in the
matter.

" But laur bless yer 'art, they got wan o'
they ole hatticrat books an' started raidin'
out a gurt ole long list o' things which the
host had got to du. I was the host yu mus'
onderstan,' an' whane they started raidin
down all the things I'd got to mind, I says,

" ' Yer, stap,' I says. ' Do yu think I c'n
keep all they things in my noddle wat yu be
raidin' down. Wy, I shid go clane mazed if
I tried to mind one-half o't.'

" Howsumever, us did'n get on so bad

D

c'nsiderin'. Us 'ad a butivul day—zin
shining all th' arternune.

"They sticked me down to the vore-geat,*
an' ev'rybody as they arrived, I 'ad to shaake
'ands wai,' an' ax how they was, an' then tell
'em they'd vind Mis's Ley into the vore-door,
an' plaize to go in, an' 'ope they'd injoy
therzels, an' zo on.

"I got on middlin' to thiky job, but o'
cuse I med wan or two mistaakes. When
Squire Goodman's carriage draived up I
spauk up jovial like to the coachman. Tom
Peters 'twaz, an', o' cou'se, I've knawed
Tom f'r the las' vowerty years. An' I virgot
like, that vokes in the Higher Circle muzzen
talk to other vokes's coachmen. Zo, o'
coose, I olleys out.

"'Ullaw, Tom,' I says, ''ow is it b' thees
time, then?'

"Aw my blassid! When my wive yerd
o't if her wad'n like wan taygur!

"Wull, as I zed bevaur, us had a matter
o' vowerty vokes there. But laur, wat a
mug's game twas to be sure. If that's wat
they caals a garden party, give me a funeral.
Twid be a sight more cheervul I sem. There
they bide, 'arf o' min, pakin' up an' down,
wishin' twas time to git long 'ome.

"'Cou'se, the young gen'lmen an' the
young laadies they injoyed ther'zels or-right.
They'd injoy ther'zels any-plaace if you
mixes 'em up together right.

"They was zune playin' this yer lorn-
tinnis. I bide watchin' o'm vir a bit.

"'Lor,' I thort to mezel, 'id'n it windervul wat a smarl thing 'll amuse zome voke!

---

* Front gate.

Jis-to-zee they girt men knackin thikky there
baal back an' vore like that; f'r all the gude
in the wordle like a passel o' skule-chillern.'

" Bim-by wan o' the young laadies comed
up to me an' 'er says,

" ' Mester Ley,' er zes, ' wull yu plaise to
come an' make up a set ? '

" ' Ees, fai I will,' I says, f'r I wiz orwiz
vond of a dance, although, mind yu, I wad'n
aware till that minnit that there wiz gwain
to be any dancin' to our party. ' Wat is it
to be ? ' I says, ' Lancers or quadrilles or
wat ? '

" My ayes ! If that did'n zet 'em all off
laafin' like billy-o.

" ' Us wad'n manin' dancin, Mester Ley,'
says young Miss Beer—Turney Beer's darter
that is—' us maned a zet to play lorn-tinnis.
Yu an' Miss Jones be gwain to play agin me
an' Cap'm Johnson.'

" ' Me play lorn-tinnis ! ' I says. ' No
thanky ! I wid'n draime o' jissy thing.
Nivver do'd jissy thing in me live, an' I be
got too auld to begin now.'

" But they wid'n yer it. Twadd'n wan bit
o' gude in the wordle f'r me to zay ' No.'
They wiz aroun' me like vlies aroun' a jam-
pot.

" ' Yu mus' play Mester Ley,' they says.
' Us'll taich 'e.'

" ' Ees ! ' thinks I to mezel ! ' You've med
up yer mind to zee me maake a fule o'
mezel, ab'm 'e, yu tormentin toads ? '

" But I knawed perfec'ly well if I did'n do
as I was axed, my wive 'ud zay twad'n hatticrat, or zome fine thing or nuther, so I thort
I'd better way give een, an' let the fules 'ave
ther' awn way. They'd live the longer vor't.

" So they pausted me up wan zide o' the net an' Miss Jones on me left-an' zide. An' auver tuther zide was Miss Beer an' Cap'm Johnson.

" Wull, then they gi'd me this yer bat thing—yu knaweth the zort o' thing—like a zeeve wai' a long 'annle. I reckon I annled 'en 'bout as graceful as a cow wid a muskit.

" ' Wat 've I got to du wi' thees yer thing ? ' I says.

" ' Hat the baal wai'n,' says the Cap'm. ' When I hat's 'en 'cras to yu, yu hat'n back to me, dawn 'ee zee ? '

" ' I yers,' I says, 'cuz I b'leeved they was aunly maakin' game o' me.

" ' Wull, now, look out,' he says, ' I be gwain to zarr '; an' wai' the saame he drawed a baal a li'l ways up in the air an' then gid'n a gude scat wi' the bat straight towards me. But he hitched up in the net, an' that stap 'en. An' very glad I was too, f'r he was coming along at a smartish paze, an' if wan o' they baals was to ketch a veller in the eye he'd knaw which eye 'twas begad.

" But I'd no· zoonder got the thort in me haid, than he let fly to another baal hard as he cude rip, an' it jis missed the top a' the net an' dapped up off the ground str'ight to my 'aid. Pon me zaul if I ad'n been purty dapper an' jerk'n wan zide a-bit, I shid 'av 'ad a black eye f'r certin—p'raps two or dree.

" But they there 'arf-fules aunly laafed.

" ' Aw, Mester Ley,' says Miss Jones, ' yu muzzen rin away from the baal.'

" ' Wat must I du, then,' I says, ' Let'n ketch me tap the nawse ? '

" Then they all laafed agean. I cuden zee nort to laaf at.

" ' No,' her says, ' hat'n back auver the
net agean wai' yer bat.'

" ' Aw ! ' I says, ' I nivver thort o' that.'
An' then the mumpaids laafed agean. Daun'
take very much to make zome vokes laaf, I
sem.

" Wull then the cap'm knacked a couple
o' baals to Miss Jones, but her was zix to he's
arf-dizzen, an' scat 'em back agean, an' then
he hat em agean, an' her zen' 'em back agean,
an' so they keeped on knackin' the baal back
an' vore, an' nuther wan o'm wid'n miss 'en if
he cude 'elp o't, cuz from wat I cude make
out arterwards the wan that misses it lost-es.
So I was watchin' they two knackin' it to an'
fro, when all of a sudden the cap'm zen' 'en
my way like a flash o' lightnin'.

" ' Look out, Mester Ley,' shouts Miss
Jones, but long avore the words was arf-
ways out of 'er mouth the baal ketched me
right bang on the end o' me nawse.

" Be dalled if I did'n zee more stars in
that instant than ever I've zeed in the sky !

" I was in two minds 'bout drowin' th' ole
bat an' ev'rything else tap o' the dung-'aip ;
but I thort to mezel I waun' be bate ; I'll be
raddy vor'n nex' time.

" An' zo I was, begad.

" I zeed the baal comin' nice an' slaw
like, an' rising jis' 'bout the heighth o' me
haid.

" ' Now,' I thought to mezel, ' if I dawn
zend yu to Jericho tiz a winder to me.'

" Zo I up wi' me bat an' I fetched 'en a
wanger—or I shid a-done only I miss 'en
altogether, an' the force I hat 'en wai' let
the bat slip clane out o' me 'and. An' if
that blassid bat did'n fly str'ight as a gun to

Cap'm Johnson's haid an' ketched 'e zac'ly
saame plaace as the baal ketched me.

"If he did'n dance around zac'ly like a
cat on hot bricks.

"'Now, then, my buty,' I thought to
mezel, "now 'tis YOUR turn to laaf.'

"But he did'n zim to zee the joke thees
time.

"Owsumever, I daun reckon he'll ax ME
to play lorn tinnis 'long wai'n f'r a bit.

"Wull—gude-bye, Tom—gude-bye, Jan."

"Gude-bye, zur. Appy Nu Year to 'e—
an' nex' time yu 'aves a garden-party mind
yu axes me," says Tom.

"Or-right, Tom," he says, "an' us'll ha' a
game o' lorn tinnis."

"No, I be dalled if us du," says Tom. "I
ban't so vond o' bein' Aunt Zally."

PART IV.

OLE Mester Ley came stroilin' up jis' as us
was all raddy to start.

"Aw, maister," says Tom, "yu 'ave raly
come, then?"

"Come, ay!" says th' ole gen'lman. "Said
I shude, ded'n I?"

"Ees, zur," 'e says. "Yu zed yu'd come in
agean thees wik, but us ded'n 'ardly b'leeve
yu mean-id to, arter that."

"Nivver rin word in me life, Tom," says
maister. "A man's word shid be he's bond,
an' that have orwiz been my rules."

"Us knaws that, Mester Ley," says Tom.
"Ev'rybody what have ever 'ad any dailings
wai' Varmer Ley knaws that when he promished a thing 'twas as gude as doan."

" Wull, an' so it shude be, Tom," he says.
" Wat's wiss than a man yu can't trist ? "

" But how many men can e' trist now-a-
days ? " I says.

" You'm right, Jan," he says. " But
'tis a pity, I sem, arter that. Wat a
vine thing twid be if ev'rybody went along
straight an' honest, sayin' wat they mean
straight out, an' nit promising naught but
what they meaned to pervorm."

" I'm feared they sort o' vokes be about
as plentiful as white hairs p'n a black cat,"
says Tom.

" 'Tes a pity," says th' ole chap agean,
" but I'm mortle feared 'tis true. But
vokes wat chaytes daun' profit by it in the
aind."

" I daun bleeve they du, zur," says Mis'
Snell.

" I be sure o't," says Tom. " Look at the
scores 'n hunderds o' cases us rades p'n the
paaper where men have putt an' aind to
thurzel's—rich gen'lmen very auf'n, highly
rispected by all thur naybers, an' looked ud
to mos' windervul by ev'rybody—an' when it
has all come to light 'an us comes to larn the
truth us vinds out that he've bin guilty o'
some ruggery or 'nuther—chayted some poor
body out o' thur money or zome zitch thing,
p'raps years n' years agone, but he hav'm
bin abble to shift it from he's mind, an' the
thought o' the wickedness he'd done grawed
on 'en to sitch an extaint that he hav'm
bin abble to putt up wai't no longer, an' so
to-last he've shat hizzell or putt a rawp
aroun' he's awn neck."

" No need to look p'n the newspaper,"
says Mester Ley, " ab'm us knawed plainty

sitch in our awn experience ? Wat about Turney Wesbury auver to Stauk ? "

" Ay, that was a mysterious caase if ever ther' was wan," I says. " Nobody nivver knawed the rights o' that avair, an' nivver waunt, I reckon."

" Nit so vast, Jan," he says. " There's a sight more volks knaws the rights o't than yu draims o' ; or that ever I draimed of either, 'till I got mixed up wi' a vew o' the gentry an' got to yer th' 'ole tale by li'l an' li'l."

" Aw I zee," says Tom ; " they knaws all 'bout it in the higher circle like ? "

" Bless yer 'art, 'ees. All the gen'lvokes around knaws the truth o't, but they keeped it to thurzel's. But as I tauld 'e avaur, zinse us lived raytired an' my wive started bein' a lady, an' gwain about to ' At 'Omes,' an' ' Garden Parties,' an' all thase yer ole kickshaws long o' the rale ladies, us have picked out a goodish bit 'bout things wat auf'n use to puzzle us when us was aunly common varmerin' bodies. An' tid'n orwiz to some o' the vokes's credick, nuther, I c'n tull 'e ; but that's nuther yer ner there, an' I daun bleeve in rinnin a body down be'ind ther' backs as the sayin' is.

" Howsumever, I'll tull 'e the truth 'bout Turney Westbury, 'cuz ther can't be no 'arm done to nobody now, for they'm all uther-ways dead or too var away for you or me to do 'em any 'arm—or gude either."

*   *   *   *   *   *

" 'Aaf-a-minit yer 'onner," says Tom, " I jis' wants to drap this yer passel into poor Mis' Partridge's door."

"How be they Partridges gettin' on now, Tom?" says Reuben.

"Aw, bad zur, shure 'nuff," says Tom. "Poor ole Zam have bin putt away agean, gone prapperly maazed he have, poor vella. An' there's missis an' they vive li'l chillern, wan in arms an' wan to foot as you mid zay. How her do live I can't think. But her's wearin' herzel all to skeen an' boan. Her goes out an' do's a bit o' work all day, an' her bides up an' do's waishin' an' ironin' an' manglin' all night. God aunly knaws when her gets a bit o' slape; but b' the looks o' 'er, I shid say 'bout wan hour a wik. An' las' wik her was carr'd up avore the magistrates an' fined aaf-a-crown fir keepin' the bigges' maid home from skule, to take care o' the baaby. This yer's a vu odds-an'-ainds my wive 'ave picked out from the rag-bag wat her thort mid come in useful to the pore aul' saul."

"You'm a liard, Tom Zalter," I says.

"Wat d' 'e mean?" he says.

"Wat I do zay," I says. "Yu zed that wat yu got in thik passel was a vu odds an' ainds wat your wive had out from the rag-bag."

"Wull?"

"Wull, an' I knaws 'tiz no-jis thing. Cuz I knaws f'r a fac' that tis all new stuff wat your wive tauld you to buy into Exter, an Mis' Salter 'ave zaut up night arter night makin' things vir they pore crayters to wear to keep 'em warm an' dacint."

"Who tauld yu that?"

"My missis was abble to tell me all about it," I says, "an' her was abble to tell me as well, that if 't'ad'n bin fir yu an' your wive

Missis Partridge an' all her chillern wid a-bin
fo'ce to go to Union 'fore now."

"G'out with 'e," says Tom, jumpin out
into the rawd. But Reuben Ley caaled 'n
back.

"Yer, Tom," he says, "yu got zummat
pookin' out th' aind o' yer passel. Dawn
look very tidy, I sem. Bit o' tape or zummat. Hold 'n up yer an' lemme stick 'n een."

So he did—but twad'n tape th'ole gen'l-
man sticked in, an' twad'n a shullin. But
twaz 'bout the saame size, aunly yaller.

*   *   *   *   *   *

Turney Westbury, as yu all du knaw, was
wan o' the most acknowledged men fir miles
aroun'. He's vinger was in ev'ry pie. In
fac', nothin' wad'n complate wai'out 'en.
Watever was to doing—to the church, or
a bazaar, or any new scheme for improve-
ments, like the seweridge to Stauk or the
Parish Room to Excombe, or the new bells
to Muddlecombe, Turney Westbury was fust
an' foremos'. He'v a-dined wai' the Bishop
scoores o' times, an' whane the Juke o' York
come to Exeter to aupen the noo Museun he
was 'long of all the nobs sticked right up
een front. He cude a-tiched the Juke all the
time he was spaikin.

Wull then o' cou'se evrybody knaws how
that wan day th' aul gen'lman was voun'
daid. The doctor zed twas 'art failure, an'
wraut out a sustificate so's the crowner
shid'n zit 'pon 'en. An' so TWAS 'art-failure
in a manner of spaikin ; but a gude doze o'
stricknin was wat med it fail."

"Es that zo ?" says Tom. "I orwiz 'ad
me doubts whe'er th' aul chap ded'n pizen
'izzel' or no."

" But wat med 'n to ? " I says.

" Yu knaws he had a zin, daun' 'e ? " says Mester Ley.

" Cou'se he had," says Tom. " Vine up-standin' young vella he was too. He went in fir lawyerin' too, did'n-a, up 'bout Linnon zum-plaace ? "

" Ees a-ded," says Reuben, " an' cou'se he orwiz reckon on comin' into a nize li'l fortin when he's vather died. Wull, from wat I c'n make out, th'ole gen'lman ad'n got the money that people attribyted to 'n. He ought to have had it mind, an' he HAD had it, but he'd lost every penny o't in some sort o' speckylation. He thort he was gwain to make a treemenyus gurt vortin all to wan strauk like, so he buyed a host o' shares in some gole mine out in Californy. But it turned out that the aunly gole in the mine was wat Turney Westbury putt into it. So he loss ev'ry varden of he's money, but he nivver told nobody, 'cuz he depainded on speckylatin' again an' gittin' it all back.

" Wull, zap'm,* he had all the manage-ment o' the fortin of a laady down Cornwall zome plaace. Her was a widder, an' had a nize li'l heap o' money of her awn, an' 'twas placed in Turney Westbury's hands, fir he to pay her the interest ev'ry so auf'n. Wull, wat did Turney do, he drayed out this yer money unknowin' to the laady (Mis' Brown, her name was) wi' the intention o' buying some more shares whereby he reckoned to double the money. Then he wid putt back Mis' Brown's money agean, an' ev'rythin' wid be or-right he c'nsidered.

---

*As it happened

"Wull, young Charles Westbury, the zin, up to Linnon, he come ingaged to a young laady naamed Miss ——, Miss ——, darn if I ant virgot the naame—'twas zome zort of a veesh——"

"Twad'n Flake, was it?" says Tom.

"No, twad'n Flake, ner twad'n dug-veesh nuther," says Maister. "Crabb, that's wat 'twas, Miss Crabb—I knawed I shid think o't in a minnit. 'Twas rayported to be a very vine ketch vir young Mester Charles, too, for her was to come into a purty li'l fortin when her gran'mother dayed.

"Th' ole man was mortle plaised yu mid be sure, 'cuz he reckoned twid bring back a bit o' money into the vam'ly to make up for wat he'd los'. An' all same time he was speckylatin' wai' the widder's money an' scheming to make a fortin for to lef' to his zin Charles. Cou'se, he went on payin' Mis' Brown th' intrest same's bevaur, so HER did'd knaw but wat her money was still saafe in the bank.

"Wull, then come the climax—an' like these things gener'ly du, ev'rything come all together. They zay it nivver rains but it powers, an' it powered down p'n Turney Westbury sure nuff. Wan day a tullygram come to zay that ole Mis' Brown 'ad died zud'nly, an' the very same day come the news that the comp'ny in which Turney Westbury had purchased all thayse yer shares had gone completely to smash. He knawed that in a vew days he'd be fo'ced to produce the money, an' he ad'n got a penny piece to shaw for 't.

"Ther' was aunly wan hope vor'n. In a wik's time he's zin Charles was gwain to be

married to the rich young lady, an' he daycided to drow hizzel' on their mercy like, an'
beg o' they to help'm out o' the mess he'd
med fir hizzel', and zave 'n vrom gwain to
jail. Nex' mornin' he had a letter from
Mester Charles zummat like this yer :—

"'Dear Vather,—

"'Cissie's gran'mother, which you've yerd
me tell about so many times, have dayed, so
us mus' prospone the weddin' fir a bit. Us
was s'prised to find that you was her trustee.
Her was a Mis' Brown, an' lived down to
Cornwall. Cissie comes into all her money,
as her have'nt got no other relations, so us'll
be well pervided for.'

"When they vound Turney Westbury, a
hour or two arterwards he was dead, an' the
doctor zed he died o' 'art-vailure. But the
doctor was a friend o' the vam'ly."

The Lazy Man.

———◆———

" DID yu raid thik bit of a skit 'p'n the paapers 'bout thikky there laazy man auver to Ireland, Jan?" says Tom Zalter the draiver.

"Ees," I says. "I DID raid thik li'l bit. Cude'n 'elp o' laafin' nuther to raid the capers he got up to, rather than he'd du a bit o' work."

"The laazy tooad," says Mis's Snell. "I'd a med 'en move 'is-sel' I bet a ap'my, if I'd 'ad aught to du wai' 'en."

"Not yu wid'n, missis," I says.

"Aw, wid'n I?" her says. "I'd let 'n zee whe'er I wid'n or no."

"Wat cude yu a-doan more'n wat they do'd?" says Tom.

"Wat wid I a-doan? I c'n soon tell 'e that, Tom. I'd a-putt a rid-ot poker where he'd zit down tap o'n."

"Yu cude'n a-do'd that," I zed, "cuz he never did'n get up. He bide in bed all the time, year in year out."

"Well then, I'd apply the poker to the same spot where he was to in bed."

"Then yu'd zet the bed avire," says Tom.

"Wull, 'n then he'd be fo'ced to get up," her says, "or else be burned to death alive. An' no gurt loss ayther I sh'd say."

"Did it putt yu in the mind of anybody, Jan, when yu was raidin' about thikky laazy chap?" says Tom.

46

"Ees," I says. "Put me in the mind of ole Noah Chilcott."

"So 't did me," says Tom. "I says to my wive drec'ly I raid it, ' Ullaw,' I says, ' yer's aul' Noah Chilcott come back agean.' "

"Wat Chilcott was that 'n Tom ? " says Jim Tozer.

"Lived auver to Norman's Cottages down b' the watter. Yu did'n knaw 'n. No, yu wid'n vir certin. He've bin daid this las' vifteen year. But he was a ronk laazy raskle sure nuff.

"Wad'n orwiz like it 's-knaw. When he was a young chap grawin' up there wad'n a listier chap 'tween this an' Barnstaple. But all of a zudden he med up he's mind that he'd done 'nuff work to las' 'en for the rest of he's live. Right in the middle o' 'ay-'arvest 'twas when he got strick like it, an' aul' Varmer Bawden so bizzy as ever cude be. Twas all sive-work in they days ; no mawing-machines. An' varmers use to be rinning zeb'm ways to-wance, to get men to do the work. So when Noah did'n turn out nex' mornen he's wive cude'n think wat-ever cude be the matter wai' 'en.

"Ar-pas' vive a-clock come, an' still he bide up-bed, so her shouted up auver stairs,

" ' Noah,' her says, ' come oan ! Du 'e knaw wat time 'tis 'tal' ? '

" ' No,' 'e says, ' an dawn keer so turrable much ! '

" ' Wat's mane, daun keer ? ' her says. ' 'Tis upright zix. Do 'e want the zin to scorch yer ayes out ? '

"Noah nivver rayturned no answer 'tal' thees time, so missis thought her'd rowsled 'en out. But ar-pas' zix come an' no Noah,

so her rished up-stairs thinking p'raps he
was tooked bad. There her voun' 'en lying
in bed so comferable as a flay in a blankit.

" ' Wat's matter,' her says, ' ban't 'e wull ? '

" But all he'd zay was to grint, an' roll
auver tother zide. So to-last, when her
found her cude'n git no sainse out o'n her
thought f'r certin he mus' be very ill. So
her putts on her bonnet an' 'way-da-go to
fetch docter. Her ad'n gone very fur when
her meet wi' a chap rinnin' as if he's live
depended on it.

" ' Aw ! Mis's Chilcott," he says, ' I was jis'
comin' up to your place. Maister zen' me up
to see for Noah. He ab'm turned up not
'et.'

" ' I knaw it,' her says, ' I be jis' fetchin'
docter to 'en.'

" ' Aw, dear. Wat's matter then ? '

" ' Dunnaw,' her says. ' He look'th brave
'nuff, but I can't get a word from 'en.'

" So her med 'aste an' told the docter, an'
docter went to zee 'en. When he come
downstairs arter 'zamining Noah all auver,
he says to Mis's Chilcott,

" ' I be feared I can't do nought vir your
'usban', Mis's Chilcott.'

" ' Wat ! ' her says, so whit's a sheet. ' Do
e mane he's gwain to die ? '

" ' No,' he says. He've got a lazy fit.
That's all the matter is wi' he.'

" Wull, Mis's Chilcott cude'n ardly bleeve
it to-first, so her carr'd Noah up he's brexis.
Her carr'd up a li'l delicate bit like, same's
her thort her ought to for a invalid like.
But twad'n many minnits avore Noah was
rattlin' tap the floor wi' a cheer; an' when
missis rinned up thinkin' he was tooked wiss,

he axed wat soort o' brexis her reckoned that
was f'r a 'ungry man. An' her was fo'ced to
let'n ha' two more sitch lots avore he was
zatisfied, an' then he turned auver an' went
to slape, like the pigs.

"Wull, from that day foorth Noah Chilcott
wid'n turn he's hand upside down to arn a
penny. He's wive was fo'ced to go out
waishin' an' clainin' to keep body an' saul
together; an' he wid ha' the best of ev'rything to ait, too. No mistaake about it. If
her did'n carr' up a fried brexis to bed to 'en
ev'ry mornen he'd laid her a dug's life.

"All the other married wimmen told about
wat they sh'd do if they was Mis's Chilcott,
an' advised her to rin away an' lef' en. But
'tis all very well to tell. Wives daun' rin
away an' lef' ther' 'usban's so aisy as that is.
At laist, not in our 'umble walk o' life they
daun'. I've yerd that amongs' gen'lvokes 'tis
no onusual thing. But our class bleeves that
wat God 'ave joined together mussen be
brauked asunder.

"Be-as-twil, poor Mis's Chilcott went on
doin' f'r her husban' an' herzel' both; an'
very soon her beginned to shaw signs o'
failing. Her pitched away to nought, an'
got to look like's if her never knawed wat
twaz to get a belly-vul.

"Wull, it got like that to-last that all
tuther wimmen cude'n stan' it no longer; an'
they 'ad a sort of a meetin' to Sal Mudge's
house. They never told nobody wat was
said to the meetin', but I'll make a bet that
ole Noah Chilcott's yers purt' near scorched
the peel-case.* An' arter it was auver, Sal

---

* Pillow-slip.

E

an' Mary Webber marched auver-'crass to Docter Gribble.

"Wat they zed to docter, o' cou'se, I can't tull 'e, but I s'pause they putt it to he in sitch a manner that he valled in wi' their views. Be that as it may, when they comed away they'd got some soort of a white powder in a bit o' paaper which doctor let 'em ha'.

"Nex' mornen they two wimmen med zome excuze to caal in to zee Mis's Chilcott jis' as her was gwain to carr' up Noah's brexis to bed to'n. 'Twas all on a tray—cup o' tay all powered out an' milk an' shugger; wi' braid an' butter an' a egg. Mis's Webber said it med her blid bile to zee it cuz Mis's Chilcott's awn brexis was on the taable—jis' a drap o' dirty watter out o' the taypot arter her'd drayed off all the tay f'r Noah, an' a couple o' bits o' dry crist. Poor saul, her tried to dray their 'tention some-place else, so's they shid'n zee it. But while her was tellin' to Mis's Webber ole Sally drapped in the powder into Noah's tay. An' then they both come away.

"Wull, bout o' tain, leb'm a-clock poor Mis's Chilcott was purt'-near frightened out of her seb'm sainses by a rumpus upstairs. Noah was groanin' an' cryin' like anybody bein' murdered. Her rinned upstairs an' voun' 'en rollin' back an' vore on' the floor.

"'Aw,' he says, 'I'm jis' daid, zen' f'r the docter, I be jis' daid.'

"Mis's Chilcott rished out to Sal Mudge's an' Sally zend her boye f'r the docter. When docter come, Noah was like anybody maazed wi' the pain. He's wive cude'n come neast 'en, 'cuz he declared her a-pisen'd 'en.

" Docter veeled 'en aul auver and shaked he's haid.

" ' I be turrable zorry f'r yu, Mis's Chilcott,' he says, so's Noah cude yer'n, ' but I be feared there's no hope f'r your 'usban'.

" ' Wat,' roars Noah, ' be I dyin' ? I knaw'd I was ! I tauld 'e so ! Her've putt pizen into me mait.' An' he broke the sheet with he's teeth, an' the swattin' rinned down auver he's faace.

" ' No, Chilcott,' says docter, ' tid'n pizen you've took. I'll tell 'e jis' wat's the matter with 'e. Your liver 'ave nearly stapped workin' cuz 'tis got all caked up into a 'ard lump. When it do stap you'll be a daid man in vower-an'-twainty hours, an' b' the way 'tis gwain on I shid say that'll be zome time to-morrow aiv'min' ! '

" Ah, my jaly. Yu shid a-yeard pore Noah then. He scritched, he zed he's prayers, he beggid o' the doctor to gi' 'en zummat to keep he's liver from stappin'.

" ' Ther's nort I can give 'e, Chilcott,' says docter. ' Ther's aunly wan thing in theas world 'ull kip your liver moving, an' that's violent exercise. If yu was to zet all your mussels hard to work, yu mid possible start off yer liver agean. Mind, I daun zay yu wude, I aunly zay yu MID. But that's aunly chance yu got. An' direc'ly yu staps, more'n, say, a hower or from that to a hower-'n-arf (sep's of a night time when you'm aslape) yer liver 'ull be liable to stap any minit, an' then you'm a dead man sure's you'm alive ! '

" Caw ! bless my art-'n-saul. In dree minits Noah Chilcott was out o' bade an' drassed an' rinnin' around lookin' vir a job ; an' ev'ry wips-wile he'd putt he's hand around to where he reckoned he's liver was to, to zee if he cude veel it workin'. He spit up dree yard o' tettie-ground thik arternune wai'out stappin' to drink—a thing he'd niver doan bevaur. An' vir years arterwads, if ever he'd bin zot still f'r a vew minits longer 'n usual, all of a zuddent yu'd zee he's hand go around to the smarl of he's back, an' bevaur yu cude zay Jack Robinson he was up an' off."

Who Stole the Donkey?

———

"WULL," says Tom Zalter, the draiver, "I spoas yu waun' be zatisfied till I've tauld 'e the whole 'istry o't. ('And out that box o' bloaters yu be zaut tap o', Jan, then I shan' want to trouble 'e agean 'genst us comes to the "Urd Lion.")

Wull, twaz laike thees yer, look'ee. Passen 'ad bin wantin a dunkey this ever-so-long. Young Master Cyr'l an' li'l Miss Gertrude grawin' up big chillern like, in a manner o' spaikin', 'e reckoned twid be a gude idaya to 'ave a donkey an' a li'l trap, so's they cude draive about to plaaces visitin' an' sitch like. 'Eed a-got the trap a-raddy. Wan o' thayse yer wat they caals goverment cars—they roundy-go things like a gurt waishin-tup sticked up on two weels, where yu staps up be'ind, an' draives out o' the cornder o' yer eye, as the boye zed.

I knawed 'eed bin wantin' a dunkey thees gudish bit, 'cuz 'e zed to me wance—an' that mus' be more'n a year ago vir certin—"Tom" 'e zes, "do 'e avver zee zitch a theng as a dunkey about in yer travels?" 'e zes.

"Laur bless yer onner," I zes, "dunkeys! ees! 'Underds an' thousans o'm."

"Wat zort o' wans" 'e zes?

"Wull," I zes, "the majority o' the dunkeys I meets wai' be two-liggid wans."

"Did 'er laff Tom?" axed Missis Snell.

"Laff, ay!" says Tom. "Sh'd think 'er did laff. 'E's a prápper nice zort is our passen. Yu kin zay wat yu mind to'n within raison. Not wan o' yer cock-tail zort wat muz'n be lookid to."

Be that as 'twull, us knawed 'e wiz on the luke-out vir a gude dunkey, an' to-las' us yerd e'd buyed wan.

Ad'n off o' zome gipsies 'e did. Gi'd vaive poun' vor'n; that's wat 'e gi'd vor'n cuz 'e taul' me zo 'is awn zel'. An' a vurry purty li'l dunkey twas too; wan o' thase yer light gray colour. Arter e'd bin clipped an' 'ad a vew gude meals inzide o'n, 'e lookid up zo smurt as a carrot, an' so peart as a banty-cock 'pon a barn-door.

But I've got avore me story.

Passen 'ad thase yer dunkey of a Vriday. I minds the day, cuz I'd then come back vrom Exeter an' was taakin' out me 'osses when I yeerd the noos. Ole Aaron Hutchins vus' tauld me o't.

"Aw-w," 'e zes, "yu ban't th' aunly dunkey in par-rish arter aul, Tom," 'e zes.

"I knaw 't," I zes. "I zeed yu standin' there dreckly as I come aroun' the cornder."

"Yu ad'n thiky time," zes Jim Tozer.

"Ees," zes Tom. "An' zo I did nex' time."

"Aw-w," zes Aaron agean, "but I manes a vower-liggid dunkey wai' long years to kape the vlies away."

"Aw, du 'e? Wull I daunt," zo I zes. "I manes a two-liggid dunkey wai' a long nawse vir paukin into other vokes's biz-ness."

"Aw, yer now!" zes Jim, "yu gi'd ole Aaron a middlin' gude scat thiky time I be dalled, vir 'e's a masterpiece vir interferin' in other people's consarns."

"That's wy I zed it," zes Tom. "I shid'n a-zed it to'n else. But 'e got prapperly vinnid 'bout it, an' purty zoon tooked hissel' off. Which as I zay, yu'll orwiz vind that the vurry people wat be most aiger to maake zome nasty raymark 'bout other vokes, be the vust to taake offence thurzel's if they thinks anybody 'ave zed the slightes' thing out o' plaace."

"That's true nuff," I says, "I be dalled if 'tidn'."

"Ees," says Jim, "but I daun' zee wat that 'ave got to du wai' the passen's dunkey. I sem yu'm gittin' all be'ind wai' the tale."

"Wull," zes Tom, "an' where shid I be wi' the tail, else? Nivver zeed a dunkey with 'ees tail in vrunt did 'e?"

'Coose, us was vorce to stap a bit an' laff to Jim tho. I tulls 'e, tidn' a scrap o' use yu tryin to best Tom. 'E sure to 'ave the las' word. Ner you can't draive'n vore vaster than ees minded to go, nuther.

"Wull," 'e zes, "passen buyed a dunkey, as I think I've tauld 'e dree OR vower times avore. An' ole Zammy Toogude wat do's odd jobs to the Rect'ry putt'n out in li'l orchid lower zide o' Jan Clattery's coort."

Yu mid depen' that young Maister Cyr'l an' li'l missie was like a couple o' maazed things auver thase yer dunkey, an' they didn' sem they knaw'd 'ow to wait till nex' mornen ardly to go vir a draive. Young maister acsh'ly beggid o'm to let 'e go to bade airlier 'n usual cuz then 'e reckoned the taime 'ud pass more quicker like.

Yu c'n make a bet they did'nt want much caalin nex' mornen—that was the Zatterday; an' they was no zoonder drassed than they

was off to the orchid like long-dugs, to zee
the new dunkey.

When they got there they cuden 'ardly
bleeve their awn ayes. Look where they
wude, they cuden zee zo much as a hoof o'n.

They sarched high an' law—the li'l maid
even looked in under the hane-coops, which
wad'n big 'nuff to 'old a dug, let 'loan a
dunkey. But no! 'Eed disappeared, that
was certin; zo they rinned back 'oam an'
tauld the vokes. Wull, then, 'coose, ev'rybody beginned to look vor'n, but the dunkey
was goo; vanished as clane as Jim Trimlett's
wages by Chewsdy mornen. Ole Zammy
declared 'e apsed the geat the night avore,
an' 'e adn' zeed the dunkey zinse.

It caused quite a consternation in the
villige yu mid be sure. Ev'rybody was
rinnin' 'bout axin' ev'rybody else ef they'd
zeed ort o' the passen's dunkey. Strangers
comin' 'long the rawd windered wat on airth
possessed the vokes—all inquirin' whe'r
they'd zeed a dunkey or no. Spesh'ly arter
passen sticked up a nawtis to zay eed gi' tain
shullins rayward to anybody as 'ud rayturn
'n ees dunkey. All the chaps waint lacin'
out auver the rawds in all dreckshins like
hounds arter fox. Young Benny Tooze
stapped a outride* draivin' in a trap.

" 'Ave yu zeed uther dunkey on the rawd ?"
zes Benny.

"Nivver till to-day," e zes. "But I be
darned if I ant zeed more dunkeys in the
las' mile o' rawd than I've zeed all the raist
o' me live putt together. Wat's matter with
'e all ?"

---

* Tradesman's assistant touting for orders.

" Passen 'ave lost 'ees dunkey," zes Benjamin.

" 'Ave er?" zes the veller. " Wull, vrim wat I c'n zee o't 'e'v got plainty more in par-rish to taake the plaace o'n."

Now as it 'appened, pore ole Aaron Hutchins 'ad bin to Brinton thik mornen to turn zome cattle vir Varmer Clattery, an' 'e got back to the villige jis' as passen were stickin up ees nawtis. Aaron axed'n wat 'twas, bein' onable to raid wai'out spullin' all the words more'n dree latters; zo passen tauld 'n, an' all bout the tain shullins rayward.

" Were it a chap wai' rid 'air an' a white 'at zold yu the dunkey?" Aaron ax'd the passen. Passen zed 'twaz.

Aaron nivver zed 'nuther word, but rished in 'ouze like as if the Boers was be'ind 'n, vixed bagginits.

" Caw bless my zaul," zes ees missis, " wat's come to the man? 'Nuff to vrighten anybody up chimley."

" Gi's a 'unk o' braid'n chaise," zes Aaron, " to carr in me 'and."

" Wy, where be gwain?" er zes. " I got a bit o' baacon an' zome vried tetties in th' oven."

" Can't 'elp o't," 'e zes. " I be gwain to zar'* tain shullins in the nex' two hours, Passen's los' ees dunkey, an' I zeed the vurry chaps wat zold'n to'n, wai' the dunkey tied up to the back o' ther' van, makin the best o' ther' way towards Barnstable. I kin auvertake they if I rins across the vields to Badden Down. That's tain shullins clane

---

* Earn.

money"; an' wai' the zaame Aaron rished
out the door an' out auver the rawd like the
devul in a gale o' weend. Nobody widn' thenk
'eed bin to Brinton an' back thik vorenune.

The plaace where Aaron 'ad meet the
gipsies was 'bout o' vower mile out, zo when
'e ketched vore to'm 'e was purty wull blawed,
yu mid be sure, vir twas a gude eight mile 'e
walked an' rinned avore 'e comed in zight o'
the van. Be thease time twas gittin dimpsey,
but Aaron cude zee the dunkey tied up to the
tail o' the van; but the wist o't was, ther'
was dree gurt men walkin long-zide; the
chap wai the rid 'air an' white 'at, wat zold
the dunkey to the passen, an' two hugly lookin' toads bezides, that med poor Aaron
shaake in ees shoes. It adn' nivver 'curred
to'n ow 'e was gwain to git the dunkey arter
e' ketched 'vore to'n, an' 'e was veared to go
vore an' zay they'd staled'n, an' demand'n
back, veared wat they'd do to'n.

Owsumever, jis then they come up to the
'aid o' the hill which they'd bin gwain up,
an' the dree men got up to raide. Then
Aaron zeed ther' was a wumman in the van
cuz 'er stap down in rawd to 'low o' the men
gittin up vust.

Aaron zeed theas was ees chance, zo 'e
waint all quiert up to the van an' un'itched
the dunkey vrom be'ind, raddy to rin like
mad if anybody inzide shid yer'n. 'E considered that the man wi' the white 'at widn'
maake a hap'ny odds 'bout cuttin' anybody's
draut an' drawin' o'n in river. Owsumever
'e freed the dunkey an' jumped pin the back
o'n, an gi'd 'n a gude cut wi' 'ees groun' aish.
Off waint the dunkey like billy-o, an' noan
o'm in the van yerd the gwain o'n.

Presen'ly Aaron meet wai' zome o' the chaps wat was lookin' vir the dunkey, an' when they zeed'n comin' yu c'n bet 'ow they did 'olley. An' they all gi'd the dunkey a gude scat as 'e waint by, an' med'n gallup an' draw up ees 'ine-ligs till Aaron wis vorce to putt ees arms aroun' ees neck, to keep on the back o'n 't al'.

They zay short an' swate like a dunkey's gallup, but I be dalled if thik there dunkey stap galluppin' till 'e carr'd old Aaron right in the villige, an' slap-bang into the middle of a crowd o' vokes, includin' the passen, polisman, an' all the villige vokes, sep's they wat was out lookin' vir the dunkey. There 'e stapped; an' stap zo zudden that Aaron waint vlyin' auver the 'aid o'n an' hat the polisman jis below ees bult, an' knack'n clane 'long the rawd.

Owsumever passen 'av got back the dunkey, an' vurry plaised 'e was too. But now the queshun was—

WHO STALED THE DUNKEY?

PART II.

AARON sim to be perfec'ly comferable tap o' the polisman; 'tany-raate, e' didn' sim in no gurt 'urry to get up. Vact o' the matter was, 'e was clane out o' broth, as the boye zed, droo the manes o' tryin' to imitate Dick Turpin. Arter a bit the bobby manidged to shiff'n, an' be that time Aaron 'ad jis got 'nuff weend back to ax passen vir 'e's tain shullins rayward.

"Wull, Aaron," says passen, "yu'm prapper'y intitled to't, ther's no gittin' away vrom it. I promised a 'arf-zovrin to whoever rayturned the dunkey, an' yu'v rayturn 'n, zo I shall be so gude's me word. If I got uther-wan in me pockit, yu shall ave'n now to wance. 'Ees, yer is wan; an' jidgin' be the looks of e', I shid zay yu'v arn'd 'n.''

Passen was jis in th' ac' of 'andin' the coin to Aaron when us yerd the mos' hawfulles' scramin' noise yu cude poss'bly imagine—a wumman scraitchin to the tap of 'er voice. 'Twaz like voerty cats wai' ther' tails in a mangle. Tull about maakin' anybody's hair stan up'n een'! Ev'rybody's 'air in thiky crowd was stood up like preckles on a vuz-bewsh—sep's the passen's, an' 'e 'adn' got noan to stand, 'cuz 'e's bal's a coot. But 'e turned so wit's a sheet I knaw, an' zo all o's did. I knaws it med me creem all down me backboan, vir 'twaz a 'orrid noise sure nuff. An wai' the zaame us turned aroun' an zeed Aaron Hutchin's wive come rishin out o' church geats, an' tare down the rawd to-wards where us was to, like anybody maazed, still scramin' an' 'er arms up in th' air, an' 'er ole kitty-bonnet, wat 'er orwiz wares, vlyin' out be'ind like the vlags to Barleycombe Fair.

Ole Martha Hutchins do's the church-claning, an' 'er most orwiz goes up zum time of a Zaturday abe'min to dist around an' zee ev'rythin's viddy vir prayer nex' day. Theas time 'er was a bit laater'n usual, an' twaz prapperly dimpsey now. But 'er was in a staate! If passen adn' ketched 'er 'olt er'd a-valled clane long the rawd, an' th' eyes o'er jumpin' out vrom 'er 'aid, 'most; an' pankin' like a unshorn sheap p'n Midzummer Day.

"Aw mai!" was all 'er cude zay, an' er'd

'ardly got breath to zay that. Aw!—aw deear!—aw mai!"

"What's matter, missis?" says Aaron, "yu'm or-right now. Wat'v 'e zeed?"

"Aw mai!" 'er goes agean. "Aw mai deear zaul!—Aw!—'E's arter me—taake'n away—Aw! Bring a baible, quick!"

"But wat es it, Martha?" says passen, "es it a goast yu'v zeed?"

"Aw, is that yu, Measta Blaake?" er zes; "aw, thank the Laurd, yu'm yer. 'E waun' come now. Naw, zur. Tidn' a goast I've zeed, but the DEVUL izzul."

"Martha, Martha!" says passen.

"Aw 'tes true, zur, I sure 'e, true's G——'s in 'eaven. I've zeed'n wai' me awn ayes, an' in church too of all plaaces; an' 'er spauk to me, 'er did."

"Spauk to 'e, Martha!"

'Ees, zur; if I nivver moves agean, an' tidn vurry likely as ever I shall, vir the live be skeared right out o' me, he spauk to me as I graupid me way up droo the church to vine me box o' matches wat I orwiz keeps in around the pulpit on the vlure, as yu du knaw, zur, yer awn zel'; cuz wan time yu stap tap o'n in the middle o' yer zarmint an' zaut min avire, an' old Mis. Weslake went into a perplexity vit cuz 'er thort 'twas the smauk comin' up out o' hell. An' 'e come right vore to me till I cude zee the vaace o'n plain as I kin zee yu now. I cude zee the two horns o'n jis like they be in the imige in ole Mis. Coombes's vam'ly baible. An' th' ole sarp'nt looked me right in the vaace, an' 'e zes, 'Martha,' 'e zes, jis like thiky there, an' the way 'e zed it, an' the way 'e lookid to me—Aw!—Aw mai!—" an' the pore old

dumman commence kickin' agean, an' scraitchin' 'till 'er drawed 'erzel clane 'long in the
rawd, an' there 'er lied lookin' like the dead.

" Poor ole Aaron's vaace was like a goast
izzel. 'E was vrightened to zee he's missis
look like it."

" I'd gi' my arf-zov'rin' willin' " 'e zed, " if
ther' was aunly a doctor 'andy."

" Eh ! Wat did 'e zay ? " zes Martha
aup'nin 'er ayes an' zittin' up so straaight as
a bade-poas. " Arf-zovrin ! Where did yu
git a arf-zovrin ? "

Aaron cude a-kicked 'izzel' for spaikin so
quick.

"Vir vindin' Measta Blaake's dunkey " 'e
zes.

" An' wat 'ave 'e do'd wai' the money ? "
'er zes.

" Measta Blaake ant let me av'n not 'eet,"
zez Aaron.

" Aw, wull, zur," 'er zes to passen, " yu
better way giv'n to me, an' then yu wull 'ave
the zatisvaction o' knowin' 'e's bin med best
use o'. But if yu let's Aaron ave'n twull
aunly be spained up to " Black Oss " in beer
an' baccy."

Zo 'er 'ad th' 'arf-zov'rin, an' arter that
'er got on windervul, an' cude zune stand up
right 'pon 'er veet. Then passen zed 'e was
gwain off to vind out wat er'd zeed. 'Er
beggid o'n not to goo ; but 'e zed if 'twaz
aunly the Devul 'issel', that wadn' nort to
be vear'd o'. 'Twas the Devul's daysiples
drassed up as C'ristians that do'd the
murchy, zo 'e zed.

An' zo, when the polisman zeed that passen
railly meaned gwain, 'e declared that 'eed
intended gwain all the time, aun'y 'e bide

there to zee that Mis. Hutchins come around or-right. 'Twaz true nuff, 'e 'ad intended gwain—but in the oppozite d'rection though. Zo then two or dree more o's volley'd on be'ind. Jo Quartley an' Billy Morrells zed they'd bide out in rawd an' zee 'e didn' excaape thiky way; an' there was a dizzen or two more o' their way o' thinkin'.

Passen got to the church door vust, a gudish bit a-haid o' the raist o's, although twadn' igzac'ly wat yu'd caal a raace arter that. Polisman let vaal a glove to the geat, an' us all stap to 'elp 'n vind'n, cuz us wid'n 'ave it zed us dezarted a veller craytur in distress. 'Twas two or dree minits avore us voun'n, an' then us discovered that 'eed accident'ly got e's voot tap o'n. Be theas time passen ad got eenzide church, where 'twas dark as a bag; an' us creeped vore to the dooar, quiet as us cude, so's not to gi' Ole Nick warnin' us was comin', an' zo gi'n a chance to excaape. Yu nivver zeed chaps so p'lite to wan tuther as us was, gwain up droo the path. Nobody didn' try to push in vrunt of wan tuther, ner eet hide the view so's tuthers cuden zee. Jim Webber bide back to the geat to hold'n aupen, zo 'e zed, in caase us wanted to pass out quick. Us didn' vind'n there when us DID pass out, ner the geat wad'n aup'n, nuther. Us cude yer the passen's vute-staps all up droo th' aisle, an' I sem'd they zounded zo 'oller as the graave. Polisman 'ad 'e's staff to 'e's 'and.

"Dreck'ly yu sees 'n," 'e wispers, a trivle shaaky I thort, "yu point'n out to me, an' if I daun' vetch'n wan 'crass 'e's tap-nat——"

My ayes an' limbs! 'Fore the words was out of ees mouthe, if didn' come the most

onairthly yell out from the church that ever
med a man's blid turn to *crid! No human
bein' nivver uttered sitch a zound. I tried
to rin, but long †mores sim to a-graw'd out
from both o' me vit into the ground. I zeed
the polisman taake wan jump auver a haid-
stone zix veet 'igh, an' go scamml'in up a
willer tree like a squir'l. Zam Arscott was
on ees knees tellin auver 'e's twice-tims-
taable under the impression 'e was sayin'
'e's prayers. Aaron an' two or dree more
was vlyin down church path like lightnin',
an' sune's I got back the use o' me vit I
tooked arter'm, quicker'n I've moved theas
las' thirty year, I warr'ner. All they wat
was stood out in rawd, when they yerd us
comin', took to ther' 'eels an' disappeared
into the 'ouzes like rabbits in a berry.

Us nivver stap rinnin' till us was inzide
the "Black Oss," an' in vac,' ontil I'd
swallered a glass o' gin an' wisky middlin
strong, I be dalled if I cude a-tauld 'e whe'r
twas Gude Vridy or Guy-Vox Day.

Presen'ly, I zes, "I be gwain back an' zee
vir passen."

"Yu kin goo," zes Ned Baaker, who was
zaut in chimleys cornder, an' kep' lookin up
chimley to maake sure th' ole Harry wadn'
comin' down, "I bant gwain to turn out o'
yer till I kin 'elp o't."

"I'll come with 'e Tom," says Aaron, "I
be 'shammed to think I rinned away like a
cowerd an' laived 'e in there aloan."

I thort more o' Aaron then than I ever did
in my live avore.

"That's zakly wat I veels," I zes; an' zo
us waint back.

---

* Curd.   † Roots.

Or us didn' zakly go back, that's tullin' o'e
a lai, cuz part ways up the rawd us meet wai
passen laidin' the Devul along be wan of 'e's
years! Twaz 'e's awn dunkey!

"Laur a-mighty," zes Aaron, more
vrightened now than ever 'er was avore,
"wat vir gudeness graashus saake 'ave I bin
and' do'd now then?"

"Staled zomebody's else's dunkey, Aaron,"
says passen, "that's wat yu've a-dude."

Us putt the two animals togather, an' zo
var's us cude zee ther' wadden a pin div-
vunce between em. Aaron stude wai wan
on each zide, "Can 'e tull me whichee is
bigges' dunkey o' the dree?" 'e zaith.

'Vore us cude tull'n, us yerd a mos' treemenyus rackit comin' long the Barnstaple
rawd, an' pres'nly us zeed a man comin'
'long p'n a oss, rattle-ta-rip hard as 'e cude
gallup. If us adn' olleyed 'eed a rawd clane
auver us. 'E stapped an' jumped off when
'e zeed we. 'Twas the man wai the white
'at!

"Ave anybody zeed a dunkey yer about?
—— wy there 'e is, or else I'm a Dutchman,
'alter'n all." Then 'e zeed the passen an'
titched 'ees 'at.

"Zarvant, zur," 'e zes. "I be turrable
plaised to zee the li'l tooad agean; an' a
middlin vine ole wile-gewze chaase I've 'ad
arter'n too, begad. Vancy 'e gettin' loose
like that. That's what comes o' lattin a
wumman tie'n up; wimmen be nivver no
gude vir tyin' knats. Ef I'd do'd 'n up mezel'
I shidn 'ad theas ole caaper."

"Ow do yu 'count vor'n gettin' away then?"
zes passen, lookin' hard to Aaron to kape e's
mouth shut.

F

" Wull, zur, yu zee 'twas like theas. They two dunkeys be two twins, an' orwiz was, cuz they was born like it, an' I spoas arter I'd zold yu the wan, 'tuther veeled loanly like, an' worked to thiky knat till 'e got izzel vree. Tes windervul wat a dunkey will du, idn' it, yer onner ? "

Passen zed 'twas, an' then advised the veller to tie'n up more secure nex' time.

"That I wull, zur," 'e zes, " I'll tie 'n up mezel, an' I make a bet 'e waunt losty tho. Gu-naight."

Arter 'eed gone passen zaut down 'pin the pump-traw an' laffed, until us was veared 'e wid 'av a vit."

"Wull," 'e zes, " if that idden zummat! Wy, Aaron, 'twas YU wat staled the dunkey arter all."

An zo 'twas. Passen's dunkey must a-manidged to un-apse the orchid geat zome-ow, an' then wander'd 'bout till 'e got in churchyard. The li'l door in the tower mus' a-bin lef' on the zam, an' 'e pushed 'is way 'een, an' the door valled together be'ind 'en.

'Twas a long taime avore Aaron cude shaw ees nawse any plaace—utherways in market or inzide a public, wai'out ZOMEBODY ballin' out

WHO STALED THE DUNKEY ?

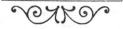

On "Baccy Smoking."

———

"DARN yer ole baccy-smauk," says Miss's Endycott. "Tis 'nuff to stiffle a dead cat. Watever a man c'n zee in a dirty ole stinkin' pipe I can't understand. Tiz zac'ly like a baby zookin' a dummy to keep 'en from scrallin'."

"Thass 'zac'ly wat I orwiz say," cheems in Miss's Snell. "There they bides, zookin' away to a bit of a pipe, drayin' in a moutheful o' smauk jis for the saake o' blawin' o' it out agean. F'r certin it can't do 'em no gude; 'cuz tid'n like's if they did ait it or drink it. It aunly goes into their mouthes an' then they blaws it out agean. I winder wat they'd zay if the wimmen was to do anything so foolish."

"Very true," says Miss's Endycott. "They'm vast 'nuff to pick out any li'l thing in a wumman to make a laffin.spoart; if 'tiz aunly the way her putt'th on 'er hat, or the way her do's 'er 'air, or any mortle thing. The men sure to ha' some silly joke or 'nother about 'en. But if the wimmen was to have sitch a stoobid, no-sense gyte as blawin' smauk out o' ther' mouthes all day long, why, gude-laur, ev'ry ole paaper you picked up wid be full o't; an' they'd make songs about it, an' I dunno wat they wid'n do."

"Now, look yer, missis," says Tom, lookin' so sayrious as a jidge, "when yu wimmin voke tries to rin down baccy smaukin' that's

67

where you makes the bigges' mistaake in the wordle. An' I'll tell 'e for why. Wimmen have got to thank the baccy for the position they holds in the wordle to-day."

"Wull mai dear 'art," says Miss's Endycott. "Did 'e yer that, Miss's Snell?"

"I yerd somethin'," says Miss's, "but I cude'n tull 'e 'ardly whe'er twas somebody spaikin' or whe'er twas aunly the weend blawin'. But I sh'd very much like to knaw how he makes it out."

"Wull," says Tom, "I was gwain to tull 'e in 'bout o' two minutes, if you cude aunly keep quiet that long. But I spaus that's purty much to expec'; wat say you, Jan?"

"Wull," I says, "I dunno much about the matter; but 'tiz a middlin' longish time for a wumman to bide wai'out spaikin', I reckon."

"Thass right. Now you start, Jan Stewer," says Miss's Endycott. Your wive daunt git the chance to talk all the time in your houze, that I'm certin o'."

"No missis," I says, "yu'm right there. Her's fo'ced to stap meal-times."

"An' then 'tiz aunly to swaller I reckon, Jan," says Tom.

"That's all," I says. "Her go'th on agean drec'ly the way's clear, like. An' manys-a-times her've scaaled her inzide wi' 'ot tettie, when her've tried to let 'en down too quick, so's I shid'n get a word in edgeways."

"Hold thee baal, Jan," says Miss's Snell. "Thee'rt a bigger vule than I took 'e to be; an' that's needless. But wat I wants to knaw is, wat Tom Zalter manes by sayin that wimmen-voke ought to be thankful to baccy-smaukin' for the position they'm een.

I sh'd very much like to knaw how 'ee makes that out."

"I'll tull 'e soon's ever I gets a chance," says Tom. "Now look at yer. Wance 'pon a time in zome parts o' the wordle, ther' wad'n no smaukin' 't al'. Baccy wad'n aiven knawed, so much."

"Very gude thing too," says Miss's Endycott, "pity 'twas ever discovered 't al'."

"'Old 'ard a bit, missis," says Tom. "Now wat was the result. You've yerd the passen tell wat I'm about to say in the pulpit, so you'll knaw tiz true, although I ban't gwain to zay that the passens is right ev'ry time. But wat was the result in they contries where ther' wad'n no smaukin'? Wy, wimmen was kep' in ther' prapper plaaces. They 'ad to go an' carr ome the watter from the well; they 'ad to go ploughin' an' raipin', an' they 'ad to grind all the corn. They 'ad to mind the sheap, an' watter the cattle, an' they wad'n 'lowed to spaik 'fore they was axed. THEY wad'n permitted to go pokin' the'r nawses into wat wad'n no consarn o' theirs. They 'ad ther' work to du an' they was fo'ced to go an' du it, an' zay nothin'. The men-folk ad'n got nort to take their minds off their business then, see; an' consequently they was orwiz abble to keep their eyes 'pon the wimmen an' zee that they did'n get out o' plaace.

"Wull, then, arter a bit, baccy was discovered, an' from that day to theas wimmen 'ave continued to rise higher an' higher out o' their prapper spear, as passen caals it. Bevore that time, when things 'ad gone wrong wi' th' ole man, he used to taake a gurt stick an' give a vew o' the wimmen a gude warmin'; an' that use to putt he right, an' do they a power o' gude saame time. But soon's ever baccy-smaukin' was invented, things beginned to alter.

"When th' ole man got irritable an' grainy like, 'stead o' warmin' a vew of he's wives, he vulled up he's pipe an' went out an' lied down under a tree an' smauked till he veeled better. An' b' the time he'd smauked a pipe-vull he'd virgot all about the warmin', an' the second pipe wid maake 'en so swit-tempered as a ark-angel. Wull, from that day vorward the wimmen got artfuller an' artfuller. When the wimmen what was to work in wan vield wanted to have a bit of a tell wi' the wimmen in the next vield, they'd laive a pipe an' baccy, or some cigars auver handy the gate. Wull, an' when th' ole man come around bim-by to zee if they was all to work, he'd zee this yer baccy an' he'd light up, 'o cou'se, an' lay down bezide the haidge, 'an mos' likely vaal 'slaip.

"Wull, then, nex' thing was, he wanted to be smaukin' an' workin' same time; but the jobs he'd kep for hissel' wad'n much gude for that. He thought to hissel' that if he were out mindin' the sheap, or 'tendin' the cattle an' 'osses, or ploughin' or hoeing turmits, or any caper like that, he'd be abble to smauk and work along the saame.

"So he says to the wimmen voke, 'I'll do the work out in vield; you git back in houze, an' vine a job f'r yerzel there.'

"An' zo they did. An' from that day vorward the men-voke do'd the varmerin', an' lookin' arter the stock an' all they sort o' jobs, 'cuz they cude smauk same time. An' the wimmen bide in houze. An' because there wad'n 'nuff to occupy their time they use to come out an' lain up agin the door-poases an' gossip to wan tuther, which they've continued to do up to the present day.

"An' they soon discovered that the more the ole man smauked baccy the better twaz for they, an' the more time they'd got for gossipin'. An' so when they vound out that he smauked more when he was erritable, then they tried to invent all the things they cude possibly think o' to erritate 'en. An' that's why wimmen erritates men to sitch extaint to the present day, but they daunt knaw the origin o't their awn-zels.

"An' zome o' the things which they invented to keep th' ole man erritable when he wid'n else, was—

"Spring-clainin, antimicassers, stiff collars, 'at-pins, blouses wat do's up be'ind, washin-days, carpets that you muzzen laive foot-tracks on, love-letters, bes' cloas, pianners, drapers' shops, milliners' bills, birthdays, picter-poas' cards, limericks, an' babies.

"When they cude'n erritate en wi' wan they tried another, an' ther' was orwiz wan or other wid make th' ole man vull up he's pipe an' go away off by hissel' to smauk, an' then they was free to go on gossipin'."

"Wat a passel o' witpot," says Miss's Snell. "I can't think how you can bide there an' tell up sitch ole rummidge. When Adam was in the Garden of Eden he did'n 'ave no baccy, did 'er?"

"No, 'e did'n," says Tom. "An' wat was the result? He wad'n 'appy, was 'er? An' the Lord thought very likely a wumman wid comfort 'en. So he gived 'en Eve. An' wat was the outcome o' that. In less'n no time they was kicked out."

"Wull, they managed to live along comferable 'nuff arter that," says Miss's Endycott.

"Very true," says Tom. "An' why was it? Ban't us told that WEED grawed up arter that. An' wat was that weed 's think. Wy baccy, o' cou'se. An' if Adam 'ad 'ad baccy in the Garden of Eden he mid a-bin there now."

The Swell Dinner.

"MY days, id'n it 'ot?" says Miss's Snell.

"Law, wat's matter now, missis?" says Tom.

"Turrable 'ot," her says. "I c'n scarcely braithe back yer."

Her was sot back in the behind part o' the van.

"Wat onraisonable crayters some of 'e be, to be sure," says Tom. "Twad'n but a wik or two agone yu was cracking off 'cuz 'twas so cauld; an' now 'tiz too 'ot for 'ee. Ther's no plaisin' some of 'ee."

"Yu nivver grumbles du 'ee?" says missis.

"Cou'se not," says Tom; "when 'ave yu yerd me complainin' 'bout the weather?"

"I dunnaw 'bout the weather altogether," her says; "but I seemed you was crackin' óff purty middlin' tuther aiv'min when I meet 'e auver to Crasscomb—when was it; las' Zaturdy wad'n it?"

"Aw, 'ees," says Tom laafin. "Ees, I was a bit niffed then, I'll admit. But that were 'nuff to make a passen sware, 'pon me saul."

"Wat was the matter then, Tom?" I says.

"Aw, I dunnaw," he says. "Nort very much when you comes to tell about it arter-wa'ds, although I was purty much putt out o' the way at the time. But tid'n weth the tellin'."

"Let's yer it," I says. "Us be the bes' jidges o' that."

"Aw, I daun mind tellin' o't," he says. . . . . . . Ther's aul James Langworthy out to he's door waitin' f'r me, lookee see. He've started he's ole capers ageanl Ev'ry blassid wik now I got to taake 'en back some ole med'cine or nuther wat he'ye zeed p'n the paaper. He rades all they ole advertysements, an' then he 'magines he've got all the complaints they tells about; an' then he buys their ole trade an' tries to pi'zen hissel' wi' 't till he rades o' some frash complaint. He nivver knaws wat's the matter wi' en till he rades the cure for 't. He's prapperly killin' hissel' through the means o' tryin' to cure hissel' o' summat wat he ab'm got. . . . . . Wull James, yer's yer new pizen; an' if I was yu I'd power it down the sink sooner that I'd power it down me droat."

"Ah! Tom," he says, "yu dunnaw wat 'tis to be bad. But I wish to gudeness yu' was gwain inwards, 'stead o' comin' home along."

"Wat for then?"

"Wy; I've jis' discovered that I axed 'e to taake back the wrong med'cine. I bin' raidin' another paaper, an' I c'n zee now wat 'tiz the matter wi' me. 'Twas my caase zac'ly. Every zimtom discribed zac'ly saame's I gets it; an' the remedy an' all. An' aunly a shillin' an' dree-appence. I thought, jidgin' by wat I raid las' wik, that twas roomadic gout that I'd got, but I zee' by wat I raid s'arternoon, 'tis kidney disaise."

"Nivver mind, maister," says Tom. "Let it bide 'fore nex' wik. By that time you'll have got summat else—maisles or whoopin'-cough, or some jis thing.   .   .   .   Kim-up Damsel—Prince-o'."

*   *   *   *   *   *   *   *

"Wull Tom," I says, wat was the li'l incident that upzot your apple-cart las' wik?"

"Wull, Jan, 'twas like thees yer. 'Twas nort but a accident arter all. Twad'n my vau't; an' yet I spaus 'twas my vau't in a manner o' spaikin; but I wid'n 'ad it occur nit for vive pound. I bin carr'ier yerfrom to Exeter a gude number o' years as yu du knaw, an' tiz a very zeldom thing that I maakes a mistaake, or causes any illconvenience to anybody. Ner I shid'n a-doan thees time if I'd minded the ole sayin', 'If yu wants a thing du'd prapperly du it yerzel'.' An', o' cou'se, to make matters wiss it mus' go an' ap'm to a man like Squire Aggett, the very las' man in the world that I shid like to offaind. He paid me zeb'm poun' tain las' Lady-day, an' that was aunly zinse Krismas; an' he's bill is nivver less'n twainty pound a year an' very auf'n auver thirty."

"He's a pippery ole toad too, min, if yu 'front 'en," says Jim Tozer.   •

"Yu'm right, Jim," says Tom, an' I 'ad a vine job tryin' to smoothe 'en down I c'n tull 'e. But I'll begin to the fore end an' tull 'e the whole rigmarole. Twas like as this.

"Las' Vriday Squire Aggett to Crasscombe Manor intended havin' a soort of a dinner party. Wull, when I say he intended having o't I mus' be careful I daun' tell 'e a lie. I dunnaw the rights o' the caase ridzac'ly, but for some raison or nuther he'd got a lot o' vokes there all onexpected.

"Be-that-as't-may, Thursdy night, 'bout

ar-pas'-nine, jis' as me an' missis was thinking 'bout gettin up auver stairs, the vootman
to Crasscombe Manor come rat-tattin' to the
dooer. Us let 'en een an' he tauld us wat
he'd come about. He's maister 'ad 'ad a lot
o' vokes come all onexpected an' he wanted
a host o' things tooked back so's he cude give
'em a swell dinner the nex' night. Wull, yu
all of 'e minds the gurt big passel I 'ad up
be'ind f'r the squire. The vootman let me
have a list so-long as yer lig—veesh, two or
dree kinds o' mait, an' all sorts an' kinds o'
vancy things vor'm to ait arter their bellies
was vull. Took me 'arf the forenoon into
Exeter givin' out thase yer divvernt orders,
an' bes' part o' the arternoon taakin em up.
Wull, wat I do'd wai'm, so's noan o'm shid'n
losty, I putt 'em all into a gurt empty box I
was taakin back, so's they shid be all in together like.

"Wull, zap'm, old Dick Radvird wat keeps
the gin'ral shop auver to Crasscombe, he let
me ha' a girt long list o' things wat he wanted
to putt in he's shop. But he's all come from
the wan plaace, there to the Stores, so I axed
'em to putt 'em all into a box so's to make it
aisier to carr'. So they did.

"Wull, when I got back so far's the haid
o' Crasscombe Lane yu can all of e mind
wat ap'm'd. I zed I'd got a load f'r Crasscombe, an' twid a-mained me gwain vive
mile out o' me way, time I'd bin to the
Manor an' back around Nerberry Coort. So
when Michael Cann come along with he's
cart leery,* gwain right by the plaace, I
thought 'twas a li'l godsend vir me.

---

* Empty.

"O' cou'se, us all knaw'th that Michael id'n igzac'ly, but I did'n think for a minit that 'twas possible for'n to maake any blunder auver sitch a simple job as that; an' yu all yerd ow many times I tauld 'en whichy passel was f'r the Squire, an' whichy was f'r 'Radvird's Stores.' "

"Yu daun mane to zay he lef' the wrong passels arter all, Tom?" I says.

"That's zac'ly wat he did du," he says.

"Au, the gurt gawk," says Miss's Endycott.

"I shid caal 'en so," says Miss's Snell.

"Wat ap'm'd, Tom?" I says.

"Wat did'n ap'm? I shid say," says Tom. "Ev'rything ap'm'd that did'n ought to. But I mus' tell 'e summat else which med ev'rything tain times wiss.

"The Vridy mornin' the cook to Crasscombe Manor was tooked very bad, an' they thort it mid be summat infectious, so her was tooked right straight away to the sallytorium. The Squire was in a purty fine hole now, sure nuff. But what he do'd, he zend off he's groom immejitly to Exeter an' had a fus' class cook back from a hotel there for the wan night. So that was or-right.

"Wull, o' cou'se, b' the time I got back, an' Michael Cann 'ad raiched the Manor twas time f'r the things to begin cooking. As I tauld 'e, that gurt, maaze-crack leff the Squire's box to Dick Radvird's an' carr'd Dick's lot on to the Manor. Dick putt he's p'n wan zide, 'cuz he did'n intaind titchin the things till the nex' day. An' o' cou'se, the new cook, he did'n knaw he'd got the wrong things, so when he tooked out the passels he was in a purty vine ole stew, yu mid depaind. He chucked the things down p'n the taable an' went straight up to zee the Squire.

"Squire was bizzy as ever he cude be, an' anxious f'r ev'rything to go right; so when they tauld 'en the cook wanted to spaik to'n he went out. The cook was lookin' turrable angry sure 'nuff.

"'I ab'm bin use to this class o' cookin', he says. 'I be gwain back an' yu mus' get zome-body else to du it for 'ee.'

Gude laur! The poor Squire vas purt' near maazed. Aunly 'bout a hower leff to dinner-time. O' cou'se he did'n knaw the wrong things 'ad bin tooked back.

"'Du yer best wi' wat ther' is,' he said, 'an' I'll double wat yu axed to be paid. I zend in a full order too. Ther's veesh, id'n ther?'"

"Aw, ees," says the cook, "ther's veesh right 'nuff."

"Wull, an' ther's two or dree kines o' mait, id'n ther'?'

"Ees', he says,' ther's plainty o' mait. An' ther's pastry, too.'

"'Very well then,' says the squire, 'yu du yer best wi't. That'll be orright. I'll double yer money."

"Wull, the chap went back to the kitchen, an' bim-by the gong-thing ringed vir dinner. In goes all the guestis an' zits down. Fust they ad zoup, which was very gude, 'cuz the cook 'ad med that hissel.' 'Twas sitch butivle zoup that the squire got quite swit-tempered agean.

"Nex' come the veesh. The waiters putt a gurt deesh down in vront o' the squire, an' when wan o'm tooked off the cover, wat's think 'twas?"

" Dunnaw, Tom."

" Blawters. I spaus from the servants' tellin, the squire was like wan roarin' lyon.

" 'Tell the cook to zend up the prapper veesh,' he olleys.

" 'Plaize, yer worship,' says the waiter chap, 'cook says that's all the veesh ther' is barrin' tinned sammon.'

" 'Taake it away,' says the squire in a faint voice, 'an' tell him to zend up the mait.'

" All the laadies an' gen'lmen was wipin' ther' nawses to drown the smull o' the blawters ; an' some o'm was fo'ced to cough to pertend they wad'n laafin.

Bim-by in come the mait. When they oncovered it 'twas this yer corn-bafe wat comes auver from Amurrica in tins, like us use to raid about in the paapers was made o' dead rats an' all thikky zort o' thing. Some of the laadies was purt' near zick, an' the squire rolled auver an' nearly 'ad a vit.

" 'That cook is tryin' to insult me,' baals the squire.

" 'Plaize, yer onner,' says the waiter fella, 'cook says if any lady or gen'lman wid prefer it ther's blawter-paaste or potted 'am-an'-tongue ; or shall he zend up the pastry ? '

" 'Take this away an' zend up the pastry,' says the squire, sittin' all to a heap, an' 'ardly knawin' wat he WAS saying.

" So they fetched up the paastry.

" 'Twas varden caakes !

" Thees time the laadies an' gen'lmen cude'n contain ther'zels no longer. They purt'near bust ther'zels laafin. I'll maake a bet zome o'm ant stop laafin 'eet.

"Nex' mornen' squire zend f'r me, an' I zoon discovered wat 'ad ap'm'd.

"Forch'nitly, Squire Aggett can zee a joke wi' any man, an' he was sune laafin' so much as any o'm.

The Best Lies Deepest.

———

"HAVE 'e yerd the latest news, Jan?" says Miss's Snell.

"Dunnaw," I says. "How long have it bin out? I've yerd that Varmer Long los' a bullik las' Tuesdy wik, an' I've yerd that Sarah James weared her las' zummer's hat to church las' Zindy, trimmed up to make 'en 'pear like a new wan. Is ther' ought later'n that?"

"Have 'e yerd that Dick Bradley got a baaby?"

"No," I says, "I ad'n yerd that."

"Wull, he hath, then," her says.

"Hath-a? That's cont'ry to what folks expected, id'n it?" I says.

"Wull, he's wive have," her says.

"Wat is it?" says Tom, "boy or a cheel?"

"'Tis a boy," says missis. "Brave, fine cheel, they say. I ant zeed 'en, not 'eet."

"Wull," says Tom, "I be very plaised to yer 't. I veel convinced 'twil be the makin' of Dick. Us'll see the best o'n come out now."

"I doubt it," says Miss's Endycott.

"Cou'se you du," says Tom. "Zac'ly like a wumman that is. They'm orwiz the fust tu b'leeve anything that's bad about anybody, an' the last to b'leeve any gude about 'em."

"Yer, steady on, Tom," says Miss's Snell.

"'Tis true," says Tom. "Coo'se, I daun say you'm all as bad as wan tuther. But

81   G

the majority o' wimmen is like it. You jis make a raymark agin somebody's character where there's two or dree wimmen about—jis' casual like. Say you've yerd that so-and-so do'd sich-an-sich a thing, but you dunnaw whe'er 'tis true or no; 'tis aunly wat yu yerd. Yu zee what they'll say.

" ' Yu mid depaind 'tis true,' they'll say. ' I veel certin sure 'tiz true. Er's jis the body wid du sitch a thing.'

" That's how they'll go. An' when they goes raypeatin' it to zomebody else, they waunt say 'tiz zummat they've yerd, and dunnaw whe'er tiz true or no. Not they. They'll zay :

" ' Yer, soce. 'Ave yu yerd about so-an-so ? Prapper scandal to the pareesh——'

" An' then away-da-go, so vast as their tongs 'll wag. An' ev'ry wips-wile they'll putt in a bit extry of their awn make-up, jis to make it a bit more tasty like."

" 'Tis no jis thing, Tom Zalter," says Miss's Endycott.

" Aw, id'n it ? " says Tom. " Spaishly if ther' 'ap'ms to be another wumman in the job. If ever you yers wan wumman givin' another wumman credic for wat her've done, wai'out tryin' to vind some bad raison under-neath, then you can depaind 'tiz 'most time to prepare for the nex' wordle, 'cuz the aind o' thees wan id'n very fur off."

" Wat's matter wi' Tom s'mornen, Jan ? " says Miss's Snell. " Got out wrong zide the bed, did'n-a ? "

" I sh'd think he did'n get out other-wan the sides," I says. " I sh'd imagine he valled out auver the foot."

" 'Ees," says Miss's Endycott, "an' knacked

he's haid up agin zummat hard; that's how
he come cracked."

"Wull," I says, "I must say wan thing.
I've yerd a gude many things said about Dick
Bradley wan time an' another."

"Have'm yu, Jan?" says Tom. "An'
wad'n the wimmen-voke the last to zay a
gude word vor'n when he turned. An' wy?
Simply 'cuz 'twas a wumman that turned
'en."

"I sh'd 'ardly knaw the fella if I was to
zee 'en," I says. "I've yerd a gude dale o'
tell about 'en; but I dunnaw no sainse to it
arter that."

"Wull, I'll tull 'e all the fac's o' the case,"
says Tom.

*　*　*　*　*　*　*　*

Dick Bradley 'ad a poorish start. He were
left to the work'ouze door in a flasket when
he were zix months' old; and nobody never
knawed who lef'n there, ner who he b'longed
to. They took 'en een, cou'se, an' soon arterwards they putt 'en out to booard 'long o'
Missis Bradley down Cawley. That's 'ow he
come to be caalled Bradley, cuz, o' cou'se,
nobody never knawed wat he's right name
was.

Wull, yu c'n know how he was dragged up
to Miss's Bradley's. Her was paid so much
a wik for'n; an' the less her cude spaind on
the cheel the more her cude make for herzel'
to buy Holland's gin wi'. An' her did get
droo some gin too, I c'n tull 'e. Her 'ad a
gude many quarts o' gin for ev'ry pint o' milk
the baaby had, I c'n 'sure 'e.

Nobody cude uv' 'ad a much wiss bringin'
up than wat Dick 'ad. An' 'eet, for all that,
he were a nice lad grawin' up. But ther'

wad'n nobody to keep'n straight. Ther' was
the old 'umman's bad example wan side, an'
nort p'n tuther zide to counterbalance like.

Or when I say nort, that's a lie. Ther'
was summat tiz true, although it did'n sim
much at the time. Dick volleyed in th' auld
'umman's vootstaps purty well; an' I daun'
zee 'ow yu cude expec' any otherwise. He
vaaled from bad to wiss, till he got a prapper
nuisance to the neighbour'ood. Folks said
ther' wad'n no gude in en—but that's where
the mistaake was made. If yu was to leave
about a lump o' goold, an' lat 'en get covered
all auver in mud, twid be redeklus to zay
ther' wad'n no gude in en, jis 'cuz yu cude'n
zee noan. An' that's 'ow twas wi' Dick.
There was plenty of gude there, min, aunly
twas cuvered auver wi' wickedness. Zimply
wanted the wickedness scraaped away.

Howsumever, come to last there were
aunly wan saul that sim to 'ave any control
auver Dick 't al'; an' that were li'l Maggie
Discombe, the gamekeeper's li'l maid to
Downwell. Her were a swate li'l crayter,
sure nuff, with a heart like butter in August,
an' chicks like apple-blossom. When folks
seed her wi' Dick Bradley they use to say
twas a pair from the nex' world; wan from
Heav'm, an' wan from—tuther plaace.

That was up to the time that Dick were
about vowerteen or vifteen, an' Maggie were
a year or two younger. Then volks beginned
to talk, wimmen voke espesh'ly, an' it come
to ole Joe Discombe's yers.

Cou'se, you knaws wat Joe is. He've got
that bumptious way about 'en as though
ther' wad'n nobody in the wordle like he,
an' as though wat he did say was law an' got

to be obeyed. Tid'n ev'rybody c'n putt up wi' that sore o' manner; so when the aul' fella tauld young Dick Bradley that if he ketched he talkin to he's darter agean he'd shoot 'en, he started layin' up trouble for hissel'.

That were jis' the very wrong way to tell to a boy like Dick. Arter that he met Maggie ev'ry chance he got. An' her, poor li'l saul, use to try all her cude think o' to make 'en gude; an' if he'd aunly 'ad zomebody like her about 'en a bit more auf'n he'd never a-went wrong like 'e did.

Wull, things went on like that till Dick were eighteen year old. B' that time he were mad in love wi' Maggie, but her, poor maid, dursen' mention he's name so much, or let her vather or mother knaw that her'd zee'd en; let 'lone spauk to 'n.

Owsumever, wan day ole Mother Westaway zeed 'em stood tellin,' to the huntin-get by Harris's copse, an' her went straight and told ole Joe Discombe. Joe were like wan taygur, an' straked out droo the lane like a madman. Afore Dick knawed anything 't al', Joe hat 'n all to a heap in the hedgetraw.

Joe's a gurt strong fella, as yu du knaw; but he'd med a mistaake about Dick Bradley. Dick got up, an' afore Joe cude raymimber what day o' the wik 'twas, he flipped around be'ind 'en some'ow an' ad'n down p'n he's back. 'Twas a trick he'd larned someplaace from some of he's no-gude companions.

He putt he's knee p'n ole Joe's chist, an' he says:

"Joe Discombe, you thank the Lord that you'm Maggie Discombe's vather, or else you'd nivver get up off your back now."

Then he disappeared, an' Joe got up an'
tooked Maggie home. An' there he keeped
her, so that her cuden zee nobody—Dick ner
nobody else.

Wull, yu knaw wat ap'm'd soon arterwards. Which o'm told the truth us'll
nivver knaw. Be-as-twull, Joe swared that
he ketched Dick in Squire's covers with
a net in the middle o' the night. Dick
sweared that he ad'n got no net, an' wad'n
poachin'—aunly taking a short cut home.
But Squire was wan o' the magistrates, an'
Dick got two months' 'ard labour. When
they took him out o' court he said:

"That's the end o' my tryin' to be gude.
Lemme get out for wan day an' I'll come
back for gude, arter I've ad vive minits wi'
you, Joe Discombe."

Ev'rybody knawed wat he maned; an' they
said he looked like the very Old Man hissel'.
Folks said they wid'n be in Joe's shoes for a
fortin.

Howsumever, bevaur the two months 'ad
passed away most o'm ad virgot about it,
speshly as hay-'arvest come along an' keeped
'em all busy. But wan aivmin there come a
man droo the plantation with he's haid down
an' the devil in he's eyes. 'Twas Dick
Bradley; an he'd no more wish to live, but
he'd got murder in he's heart. Yu knaw
when yu'm havin' a tooth drayed it seems
like all the toothache you ever had all comin'
to wan haid. An' so, on this aivmin, all the
wickedness that Dick had ever yerd, or seed,
or larned, seemed to be all gathered together
to wan boilin' in he's chest an' haid.

An' so he went on, nit too vast, 'cuz he
wanted for it to be dark when he come there.

'Twas 'bout o' leb'm o'clock when he got
fore to the tap o' the copse, cuz he knawed
the Discombes was early bed-goers, so he
expected ev'rything quiet. But all of a
sudden he yerd a most turrable noise, folks
scraimin' taps their voices, an' wi' the saame
he seed a light droo the trees. He rinned
he's hardest till he come to the lane droo the
same huntin'-get. An' then he seed drec'ly
wat 'twas. Joe's house was afire an' burnin'
like a box o' matches. 'Twas a old timbern
houze with a thatch roof, and it was blazing
like as if 'twas med o' paaper. Folks cude
du nothin' but stand an' stare.

Dick had wan look an' then darted fore
to where the people were stood.

"Where's Maggie," he says, with he's eyes
most out of he's haid. "Is her in there?"

Wi' the same somebody come rishin' fore.

"Dick," says Maggie, "aw Dick. Thank
God you'm come. You'll save vather, I knaw
you will. None of these 'ull save him, an'
they waunt let me go. They hold me back,
an' he's burnin' to death, Dick. Aw,
Dick——"

Her was clingin' round his neck. But
Dick's face was summat to see, I c'n 'sure 'e.

"Where's your mother?" he says.

"Her's away stoppin', Dick. An father's
burnin' to death. Dick, aw Dick. Daunt
look like that. He's my vather. No one
will save him for me."

Her valled down in a faint. An' they wat
zeed Dick's faace say they nivver witnessed
nort like it in their life. It simmed like
changin' from black to white.

Two men zeed what he was on upon, an'
med a grab at 'en. But 'twas no gude. He

flipped out of he's coat an' left 'en in their 'ands —— wan sleeve apiece. In a second he was buried in vire—and grown men bust out cryin'.

" Us'll nivver see either o' they agean," they zed.

But they was wrong. Afore they'd got time to think 'ardly, they zeed a black plaace in the vire, an' that was Dick Bradley wi' Joe Discombe's body across he's two shoulders. He vaaled along with he's cloas all to a flame o' vire, an' the men wat rished 'fore to drag min out was purt' near roast. For dree months they two lied zide b' zide between life an death, an' they both 'ad the wan niss

* * * * * * * *

So Dick's got a son, 'ave he? Wull, wull! Let's haup he'll make so gude a man as he's vather.

Spring Cleaning at Jan Stewer's.

———

"TOM," I zes, "can yu tull me wy 'tis ev'rything gits zo turrable dirty an' bissly all to a suddent, theas time o' the year?"

"Dunnaw wat you'm tellin' about Jan," zes Tom Zalter, the draiver, "can't volley 'e 't al'. Explain yerzel'."

"Wy," I zes, "I wants vir zumbody to tull me 'ow 'tiz that ev'ry mortle thing in a body's 'ouze—ev'ry ole nook an' cornder, ev'ry box, drayer, an' cubbord, when comes a vu days avore Laady Day gits chuck vull of muck an' dirt; an' ev'ry square voot of carpet an' ev'ry blassid picter in the plaace gits bissled all auver, till tidn' vit vir a peg to lie down an' roll tap o'. Ow kin 'e 'count vor't 't al'?"

Tom lookid to me as though 'e was makin' up he's mind whe'er 'e adn' better-way turn he's 'osses 'aids aroun' an' draive so var's Exminster or no, an' lef' me to the County 'Sylum.

"Dunnaw as ever I nawticed it, Jan," 'e zes.

"Cou'se yu nivver nawticed it," I zes; "ner 'eet I an't nawticed it, nuther. But that's zimply cuz us be men-voke. If us was wimmen us 'ud nawtis it vast 'nuff."

Tom lookid aroun' to Missis Snell.

"Can 'e tull a veller wat's matter wai' Jan 't all missis?" 'e zes.

"Matter, wai'n? Ay!" zo 'er zaith. "I knawth wat's matter wai'n wull nuff. 'E's missis bin spring-clainin', that's wat's matter wi' he."

"Haw, that's it, is it?" zes Tom, an' 'e laffed till 'e was black to the vaace.

"Spring-clainin' d'e caal et?" I zes, lookin' aroun' the van. "Spring-clainin' sure nuff! Th' awnly spring-clainin' I kin zee 'bout it is, that ev'ry time I wants to go in 'ouze I got to spring clain auver two or dree boxes, a waish-stan' an' a mangle. Wull, there, I daun' go in 'ouze no more'n I'm force to, cuz I'm jis' so likely to putt me voot into a bucket-vull o' glassen ornaments off the parler mantlepiece, or git a scat in the vaace wai' a white-waish brish, as ort-else. I've yerd it zed that a Englishman's 'ouze is e's castle; but that dawnt apply to when he's missis is spring-clainin'. 'Tis more like he's dist'ole, tho.

"Spring-clainin' Tom," I zes, "is a disaise, zame's the maisles, or mumps, or theas yer Timothy-Titus, or watever 'twas caaled, which was all the go a year or two agone, arter the King 'ad it, but it sims to be gwain out 'o vashin agean. An' when a woman shaws the simtums o't, 'er ort to be tooked right away to the sallytorian, until the vit 'av passed off, an' 'er'v got the better o't. Ther' ort to be 'sylums built spesh'ly vir wimmen, wat 'ave got the spring-clainin' faver, where they can be shut up saafe till 'tis auver. An' they shid'n be 'lowed to zee a box, ner a cubbord, ner a bit o' carpet p'n no 'count.

"Spesh'ly the carpet, Tom. Vir if a wumman ketches zight of a bit o' carpet when 'er'v got the spring clainums, 'tiz all up, carpet 'n all. 'Er'll rip'n up jis' as though it 'ad do'd 'er zome injury. Tull 'bout stappin' to taake out the nails—not 'er waunt. 'Er'll ketch'n 'olt to wan cornder, an' 'er'll give'n a haive like as if 'er was gwain to haive up Mount Arryrat an' putt'n down in middle o' the River Jordan; an' ev'ry plaace where ther' was a nail droved een, there yu'll zee a scrip o' carpit 'bout the zize o' a vive-shullin' piece. That jis' plaises 'er Tom—'er's as daylighted when 'er yers the things rippin' an' tarin', as the cows be to yer the turmot cutter. 'Tis music to the years o' 'er. An' the more 'er yers the things crackin' the more work 'er thinks 'er's doin'. An' when 'er zees the dist an' smeech which 'er'v kicked up, vullin' up the 'ouze 'nuff to stiffle a daid cat, 'pon me zaul it putts more joy into the heart o' 'er, than a quart o' zider do to the draut of a harvester.

"An' then, Tom, 'er'll 'ang up thiky pore bit o' carpit, wat niver do'd 'er wan minnit's 'arm ever zinse 'twas a carpit, 'er'll 'ang 'n up crass the cloas-line, an' 'er'll taakes yer bes' walkin'-stick, an' lat into 'n wi' thik, vore-strauk an' back, till er've brauked the stick all abroad to matches, an' bate the carpit that theen, till yu kin look right droo'n an zee the time b' the church clock. 'Tis true, Tom, true's yume there an' I'm yer; er'll do more injury to thik carpit in arf-a-nour o' spring clainin' than arf-a-year o' ord'nery ware 'n tare wid.

"Nex' thing 'er do's is try an 'zee 'ow many things 'er kin stand up, wan tap t'other, in the landin up haid o' the stairs, wai'out th'awl lot vaalin' down auver; like the chillern do wai' thase yer toy bricks. 'Er'll start wai' a box stude up 'pin wan aind so's to maake it look more clivver like; then tap o' that 'er'll putt th' 'aid o' the bed, lied vlat, an' then the drassin' taable wi' the ligs o'n sticked up in th' air. Tap o' that agean er'll 'ave a waish-an' baasin an' jug, a zaup-deesh, an' zivver other cloamen things bezides; an' tap o' the lot er'll stick the lookin' glass.

"By thees time er've discovered that the dister 'er wants to use next, is in under the box down bottom o' thase yer himitation church staiple wat er've erected. Zo then 'er tries to taake'n out wai-out disturbin wat Turney caals the equal-Abriam. An' zo 'er haives up wan cornder o' the box an' expects all the remainder o' the things to bide where they be to, till er've done pushin o'm about. An' when th' awl box o' tricks comes down tap of er 'aid like a thousan' o' bricks er looks surprised, as though sitch things didn' ought to be. An when yu come'th 'ome er'll zay twas all your vau't cuz er axed 'e to bring 'ome a bar o' yaller zaup an' two pennard o' long nails las' Vriday an' yu nivver bringed nuther wan o't. Tidn' a bit o' use vir yu to ax wat divvurnce twid a med to the things vaalin down, if yu'd thought to take 'ome the yaller zaup an' the nails. Yu muzzen nivver try to arg' wi' a wumman when 'er's spring-clainin'. Mos' likely 'er've brauked the waish-an' baasin an' the jug all to shords, an' knacked off sivver 'annles o' things, but 'er waun' matter o' that in the laistes' bit so long's er ab-m crack the lookin glass; which wid a-maned zeb'm year bad luck.

"But wat gits auver me, Tom," I zes, "is

why the things shid get into theas yer dirty
staate all to wance. Arter ev'rythin' 'ave
bin all nice an' tidy an' comferable all droo
the winter—right back as yu mid zay ever
zinse las' Laady-day, wy shid it git vulthy
durty all on a zuddent wai-out any warnin'
like? Tidn' to zay it come like it gradule, a
bit to a time like.

"Jis' taake my plaace now vir axample.
Las' wik my missis's cousin paid us a visit
an' stapped a couple o' nights. That's 'er in
to Witheridge. I derzay yu've yerd me tull
'bout Zimon Tooze—wull, he's wive.

"Wull, ther' wadn' nort matter wi' the
plaace when 'er was stappin 'long-a-way-us.
My Ann iscoorted 'er aul auver th' ouze,
vrom the vore door-stap to the li'l plaace up
'ome to the roof where I kips me woord*
apples. 'Er shawed 'er into ev'ry room us
got, 'an aunly too daylighted, cuz 'er knawed
Mis. Tooze's rooms upstairs be all white-
waish walls, an' no vireplaace in any the
baderooms, whereas us got two baderooms
wi' graates, an' all the waals paapered. Yu
knaws 'ow the wimmen vokes likes to shaw-
off their rooms to wan tuther if they thinks
they got aught a bit supayrior like.

"But, as I zay, nothin' wadn' zed 'bout
aught bein' wrong tho'. But laur-a-massey,
two days arterwads, right in the middle o'
braxis, my Ann zuddenly discovered that the
plaace was like a peg-sty. Prapperly on-
stummickable 'er zed 'twas, zo's it prapperly
turned 'er off 'er vood. All the years er'd
lived in the 'ouze, 'er reckoned 'er'd nivver
zeed'n in sitch a bissly, vulthy, dirty dis-

---

* hoard.

graaceful staate avaure—which is zacly saame
as 'er zed las' year theas time, an' the year
avore, an' the year avore that, an' the year
avore that agean, an' so long back as I kin
mind. I zeed wat was the matter, an' wat
the complaint was 'er was sufferin' vrom—I
knawed 'er was gwain to 'ave a attack o' the
spring-clainititus. I thought p'raps I mid
prevent it if I tooked it in time—nipped it
in the bud, as the sayin' is. An' 'eet I ought
to a-knawed better, arter all thase years.
'Wat's matter wi' the plaace?' I zes, 'I daun'
zee nort matter wai't. Wy twiz awn'y
yesterdy I was thenkin' 'ow clane an' butivul
ev'ry thin' did look'—which I spoas is the
saame lie as ev'ry married man tulls under
the saame circumstances."

On Spring Cleaning.

"WULL, Jan, zes Tom Zalter, " 'ow 'ave 'e got on wi' thiky-there spring clainin' job up to your houze? Have 'e mos' vinished wi' 't?"

"Aw, ees, Tom," I zes; "us 'ave got auver 't till thees time nex' year, I spoas. But 'twaz a sharpish attack while 't lasted, begad."

"Wiss 'n usual, Jan?" zes Jim Tozer.

"Wull, I dunnaw 'bout that," I zes. "I daun' spoas 'twaz any wiss 'n usual, not reely. Aunly 'twaz like ev'ry other complaint. Yu orwiz fancies the wan yume sufferin' from at the time is wiss 'n any other. When yu've got the toothaache yu'm positive ther' iddn' no pain so bad as the toothache; an' then when yu gets the back-aache yu declares the back-aache's the wist pain in the wordle. An' 'tis zakly saame wi' the haidaache or the stummick-aache. The wist pain of all is the wan yuve got at the time. An' 'tiz windervul ow' much aisier tiz to bear vorty aaches an' pains wat other vokes 'ave got, than 'tiz to putt up wi' wan that yu'm zufferin' vrom yerzel'. But I'll tell 'e wan thing soce, an' I daun care," I zes, "if yu tulls it to the 'awl par-eesh, an' that is this yer; that I be darn glad ther' idden but wan spring in the year; vir if ther' was any more, I be dalled if I widn' go out an' live 'long o' they haythen chaps out to Some Plaace, wat thik

95

mish'nary chap showed us with e's ole majic-lantern up skule; they wat cude make nuff cloas vir th' awl vam'ly out of a ole pocket ancher; an' did'n build no houses vir therzels, but lives in the loo of a gurt rock."

" Dawn they du no spring-clainin' out there, then, Jan? " axed Tom.

" I did'n yer 'n zay as they do'd any zoart o' clainin' 't al'," I zes, "an jidgin' be the looks o'm, I shid zay they didn', nuther; but laur, bless yer art soce, I reckon wimmen be purty much the zaame aul the world auver. I derzay aiven they out there vines zome excuse or nuther to laid th' ole chap a dance wance a year. Yu mid depend 'pon it, the wimmen haythens declares when the prapper time comes aroun', that their pa'tickler rock 'ave got bissled up wi' the rain an' the mud till they'm 'shaamed to zee 'n, an' the marks where the snails have crawled up auver, an' the burds an' things—they swares an' declares they nivver zeed 'n in jissy staate avore, an' nobody's else's rock vir tain miles aroun' is quarter zo dirty as wat theirs is.

"An' then they 'sists out the pore ole man an' starts drawin' buckets o' watter all auver the rock, an' all auver ther' own zel's (more auver therzel's than auver the rock if they'm ort like the wimmen voke be yer-abouts when they tries to do a bit to whitewaishin). An' arter they've spoiled the look o' the rock an' knacked off a vew of the cornders, they starts rectifyin the spot where the ole man lies down to o' nights, an' they frash arranges it so's ee'l be vorce to putt 'ees haid wher' 'ees vit used to be. An' all the dashels*

---

* Thistles.

which the pore baggar 'ave spaind the las'
twul' months in gittin use to, an' on'y jis got
min wat yu mid caal comferable like to lie
tap o', by rollin' 'pon 'em nights till they've
lied down flat, they turns min all auver, an'
arranges min all careful wi' the preckles
upperds, cuz they says they look purtier that
way, an' tiz a change; an' ev'ry night vir a
vortnit the pore ole blid drames 'e's a vuz-
pig* with 'e's skin putt on in-an-out. 'Tiz
windervul," I zes, "'ow wimmen du love to
'ave a chaange. When a man gets a thing
to 'e's liking, 'e prevers to let 'n bide there,
an' widn' 'ave 'n disturbed p'n no 'count.
But wi' a wumman 'tiz divvurnt. 'Er's for
ever wantin' to zee 'ow the things wid look
if they wiz zome-plaace else. An' that's the
rale raison, you, wy 'er 'aves a spring-clainin'
wance a year. Tidn' 'cuz the plaace be durty,
not a bit o't, 'cuz er'v bin scrubbin' to't, an'
rubbin to't, all the year round, so it stan's to
raizon it cuden possibly git in the staate 'er
maakes out. All this yer ole rigmarole bout
the durt an' the dist an' sitch like, 'tis on'y
axcuse 'cuz 'er wants to putt the bed wi' the
haid around tuther way, an' 'er wants to zee
'ow the waish-stan' wid look if 'er was to
putt'n wher' the drayers used to be. An' the
nex' time yu goes to bade if yu shid apn' to
go in the rume in the dark thinkin' yume
gwain to walk straight 'crass same's usual,
yu hats yer vute up agin the ligs of a taable
wat use orwiz to be in vrunt o' the winder,
an' maakes yer taws crack agean. An' then
they winders that a man zes things 'e didn'
ought to."

---

* Hedge-hog.

H

"I daun zee wat yu wants to blaim the wimmen zo vor," zes Missis Endycott, "when they tries to do ther' bes'."

"Bless thee zaul," I zes, "I baint blaimin' o' the wimmen. 'Cuz vir wy? They can't 'elp o't. An wat's gude o' blaimin' anybody vir wat they can't 'elp o'. Yu mid zo wull blaim the pig vir curdlin' up ees tail. Wull there, I spoas it keeps min out o' wiss wickedness. If they didn' 'ave spring-clainin' wance a yer to lat off stame like, laurd knaws wat murchy they mid get into."

"Wull, wat did 'em du to 'e Jan, wi' all o't?" zes Tom. "Us ant yerd the rights o't now, 'cuz las' wik yu jis got zo var, an there yu sticked like the boye wat vaaled in the barreel o' traicle."

"Aw," I zes, "I dunnaw as they do'd much, in a manner o' spaikin. I derzay yu knaws wat 'tiz like so wulls I du."

"Can't zay I du, Jan," zes he; "my lodger daun du much in that line—meanin' to zay not to go in vor't to a purpose same's yours du, if yu understan' me."

"Wull, you zee," I zes, "'tiz like this yer wi' your missis, Tom. 'Er's wan by 'erzel', an' wher' the'rs wan wumman be 'erzel' like that, 'er nivver goes in vor't zo rash like. Yu wants two o'm, be gude right: or as many as you kin git vir the matter o' that, an' then they tries to zee witchee kin maake the mos' noize, an' git the mos' smut 'p'n' 'er vaace. Same's I zed avore, spring-clainin is a dizaise, like the smarl-pox or influenzy, an' if ther' idn' nobody to ketch it, tidn' a bit o' gude 'aving o't."

I zeed Missis Parkouze was gittin' warmed up like, an' I was 'spectin' ev'ry minnit to

zee 'er boil out auver, 'cuz I'd bin watchin'
o'er out vrom the cornder o' me eye like, an'
I'd bin lying o't on zo thick's I cude, zame
purpose to zee 'ow much longer 'er'd go on
wai'out bustin', 'cuz I knaws 'er's a maister-
piece for spring-clainin.   Pore ole Jan
Parkouse told me hiszell wan-time that 'e've
sleeped in the tallet avore now to keep out
the way o't till 'tiz auver.

"Yu'm tellin' like a fule," 'er zed to last,
when 'er was veelin' like a barreel o' beer
wat bin corked up too zune.   "Wat du yu
knaw 'bout keepin' a 'ouze clain," 'er zes.
"Yu men be all zac'ly alike.   Yu jis' comes
into yer mails and' 'specs to vind ev'rythin'
in apple-pai order, an' raddy to a minnit's
nawtis, an' us pore wimmin—"

"Do's nothin'," I zes, "but slave an' toil
vrim vus' thing o' mornen 'to las' thing o'
night wi' nivver a' moment's plaisure, ner a
zingle minnit's rest vrom days-light to
dark."

"'Ow did yu knaw wat I was gwain to
zay?" 'er zes.

"Bless yer 'art missis," I zes, "I've yerd
it zo many hundreds o' times that I knaws it
all off be rote.   But theas yer spring-
clainin' is nort else but a ole superstition
yer knaw."

"Wat du 'e mane by yer superstition," 'er
zes.

"Wat I zay," I zes.   "'Tiz nort else but
a ole superstition wat bin handed down vrim
wan gineration of ole wimmen to the nex',
from time in memoriam; that when a certin
time o' the year cometh around, ev'rythin'
in the 'ouze wat's capable o' bein' moved
'tal', got to be tooked up, turned tap-an-tail,

twisted in-an-out, knacked wi' a 'ammer, carr'd out to the vore-dooar, gi'd two kicks an' a shaake, carr'd back in agean, an' zaut down to a divvurnt plaace to wat t'was avore; so's anybody wat wants it shant knaw wher' to look vor't, an' ev'rybody wat daunt want it shall vall auver't."

Ententes All Round.

" I DAUN' caal 'tis vair," says Tom Zalter
the draiver.

"Wat's that idden vair, Tom?" I
says.

Tom 'anged up the reins to the hook in
the tap o' the van, an' let th' osses goo 'long
be therzel's.

"Wy, I bin raidin' thees yer paaper—or
jis scanned it down auver, an' I zee the
Linnon County Council chaps ave all bin
'avin a 'ollerdy auver to Vrance, long o' the
Par-is County Council. An' purty vine ole
times they bin 'aving auver there, too, be
wat I c'n sainse o't."

"Didn' I zee zummat 'pin the paapers a
bit agone 'bout the Vrainch chaps comin'
auver yer to Linnon?" says Dan'l Widdon.

"Ees, cou'se they did," says Jim Tozer.
"Artvul bit o' work I reckon that was, 'pin
the part o' the Linnon chaps, axin' they
Frenchies auver yer, 'cuz they knawed vurry
wull they cuden du nort else but return the
compliment an' ax 'em back agean."

"I nivver yeard nort 'bout that then," says
Tom.

"I derzay yu didn'," says Jim, "ner 'eet
shidn' I a-doan, nuther, I daun' spoas, on'y
as 't 'appened, that wik I wiz force to carr'
Mis Snell's mait een me lap, cuz 'er'd a-got
zo many passels else, an' 'er didn' care 'bout
puttin' o't 'pin the vloor seemin', an' there
was all the vull 'count o't down 'pin the

paaper wat was around the mait; so as I adn' got nort better to du, gwain 'ome-along, I raid th' awl rigmarole an' pedigree o't."

"Wat did'm du then, Jim?" says Tom.

"Aw! I dunnaw 'ardly now, wat they DID du, I've mos' virgot. They was s'posed to come auver to zee 'ow things was manidged to Linnon, an' try an' zee if they cude'n pick up a wrenkle er two, to carr' back 'ome long-a-wai'm. But zo vur's I cude zee, most o' ther' time was took'd up rinnin' bout to theayters an' music-alls, an' gwain out to banquits an' denners. Pon-me-zaul the quantity o' lunches an' denners, AN' banquits they vellers did ait—wull there, I shid think be the time they got back to the'r awn plaace they was ashaamed to look a cow in the vaace."

"Wull," says Tom, "an' from wat I kin pick out from thees yer ole paaper 't 'ave-a-bin purty much the saame auver to Par-is wai' the Linnon chaps. They bin auver to pay a soart o' return visit like, seemin, an' I be dalled if they 'ant 'ad a middlin' ole vrawzy now, wat wi' wan an' tuther o't."

"Raid'n out yu," says Dan'l.

"Bless thee 'art," says Tom, "daunee tull nort 'bout raidin o't out! Gude laur, tiz sitch ole jaw-breakers I can't make out but wan word in zix."

"Wull, raid wat yer can o't, Tommy, an' wat yer can't raid, spull."

"Orright," says Tom, "lets zee wat us can do towards it. 'Tis wraut up auver:—

"'LEN-TENT MUNY—MUNY—MUNY,' zummat er nuther. Dalled if I kin raid the word. I daun bleeve TIZ a word. 'Tiz zumbody's make-up, I shid thenk."

"Le's I zee," says I. Zo Tom raiched auver the paaper an' sticked ees vinger 'p'n the word. 'Twas

L'ENTENTE MUNICIPALE,

watever that mid be. But I wadn' gwain to let 'em think I didn' knaw nort 'tal', so I says:

"Wull," I says, "jidgin be the shaape o't, I shid zay tiz Vrainch. Lets tare 'n abroad a bit, an' vine the meanin' o't. Thur's a HAM (M), an' a YEW (U), an' a HANE (N), to the vore aind, and that's MOON vir certin; an' ther's a PAI (P), an' a HAY (A), an' a HUL (L), an' a HEE (E) to the tail aind; an' that's PALE, idn' it? meanin' to zay 'twas all pale an' white in the moonshine. Wull 'n, in the middle ther's HI (I), an' a SEE (C), an' a HI (I), an' that's ICY. So I shid zay 'tis meanin', TWAS VULL MOON AN' DOOSTED COLD."

"Orright," says Tom, "us'll let it bide to that. An' it daun' make a gurt lot o' odds if 'TWAS cold, vir they ad plainty o' the stuff wat kips 'e 'ot, sims so."

"Wull, lets yer wat they do'd, Tom."

"Laur, bless thee 'art," says Tom, "I shidn' get droo wai't in a month o' Zindys; not if I was to putt on tain pairs o' spar-ticles. They waint auver to Vrance pin a Mondy, simso, in a ship."

"Wull, us didn' spoas they walked auver," says Jim.

"Yu putt yer thumb in yer mouthe a minnit er two, Jim," says Tom. "They mid a-went auver in a balloon or a vlyin' machine, vir ort yu knaws. Wull, be-that-as-'twull, yer's the program of all wat they do'd.

"Mondy they 'ad a banquit to the Hotel Devil."

"Hotel, wat?" says Miss Endycott.

Tom spulls it out a letter to a taime.

"D-E-V-I-L-L-E. What can 'e make out o' that else?" 'e says.

"Wull there" 'er says, "ther's no 'countin' vir tastis, spesh'ly wi' thase yer vurriners."

" . . . which was volleyed by a conzert," Tom raid on. "Gude beginnin', begad. Banquit vurry vus' start off."

"'Chewsdy. The visitors were taken vir a draive droo the main throughfares an' visited the Pallays de Jistice, an' the—someplace else—an' the Pallays de—de Bux Harts (watever that is—Laurd knaws I daunt). They then proceeded by way of the Avenue—dez—Champs Ely-zees an the—an the Boys de Boo—boo—logney (gude laur who the diggens wid be a Vrainchman, an' 'ave to talk all that ole trade) an' to the Jardin d—d—Axclamation, where lunch was zarr'd. There you be! I knaw'd us'd come vore to thik lunch purty quick. Wull, thur's a host o' other plaaces they waint to, an' vinished up to the hopera.

Wainsdy the same—lunch some plaace else an' a baal to the Hotel Devil agean—Thursday the saame all auver agean—lunch agean some place else—Vridy the saame agean, an' vinished up wai another banquit, an' then all trapesed off to the theayter. I caals that a middlin gude wik o't—taken into c'nsideration they bein' 'pon bizness an' all. I shidn' mind doin' a week's bizness that way mezel'."

"Wull, but Tom, 'ow do yu make out tidn' vair?"

" Wy, 'cuz tid'n. Luke yer ! Wy shid Linnon vokes git all the privilidges like that. Wy shidn' the contry plaaces git a look een zum-times ? Vir instance; wy shidn' Muddlecombe Par-ish Council taake a trip auver to Vrance, an' visit zome Par-ish Council auver thair, an' larn a thing or two, an' then ax' they back agean ? "

" Aw-w ! now yume tullin' ! " says Jim.

" Wull, I knaws I baint wis'ling, ner 'eet zingin," says Tom. " I be awn'y tullin wat ort to be. Zee 'ow vine twid look all the vul 'count o't in the ' Western Wikly Noos,' " an' Tom med wise to be raidin off from a paaper.

" Hark at yer'."

MUDDLECOMBE PAR-ISH COUNZIL.

VISIT TO VRANCE.

" ' MONDY—Muddlecombe Par-ish Counzil lef' Muddlecombe vir Plymouth, preceded in vrunt be the Barleycombe brass ban'. Weel Brewer's wive lat 'n 'ave zixp'nce to spaind. Jan Stewer's missis widn' lat 'e goo 't al', veared some Vrainch maid or 'nother 'ud rin away wi'n. Mester Dan'l Widdon med he's weel, in caase anythin' shid 'appen to 'n, an' 'e shidn' come back agean ; an' Turney Gurney putt a vlask o' brandy in 's pockit vir the saysickness. Mis. Cobley do'd up her man a passel o' zan-widges an' a pig's yer, cuz er zed the Vrenchies widn' gi'n nort to 'ait 'sep frogs.

" ' CHEWSDY.—The Muddlecombe Par-ish Council arrived in Vrance an' 'ad a banquit. Arterwads they waint to the theayter.

" ' WAINSDY.—The Muddlecombe Par-ish

Council waint to Theayter vust, 'an 'ad the banquit arterwards.

"'Thursdy.—The Muddlecombe Par-ish Council waint to Theayter an' tooked ther' banquits in their pockits. Dan'l Widden tooked ees in he's hat, 'cuz 'e reckoned twid 'old more; Dan'l 'avin a bewshul-baskit soart of haid.

"'Vridy.—The Muddlecombe Par-ish Council 'ad a banquit an' then come back 'ome.

"'Zatterdy.—The Muddlecombe Par-ish Council be all bad, up-baid.'

"Then the nex' thing us'd 'ave, wid be the return visit o' the Vrainch Par-ish Council, Then yude zee 'nuther vull 'count o't in the 'Western Wikly Noos,' zummat arter theas style,—

"'Mondy.—Vrainch Par-ish Council arrived, an' was meet outzide the villidge by the Muddlecombe Par-ish Council led by Uncle Tom Cobley in ees box-'at—same box-'at wat ees vather an' granfather weared avore'n. Arter they kissed wan tuther all the way roun', Uncle Tom wiz abble to swear that all the Vrainch chaps 'ad bin aitin' ingyens 'seps two. Then they marched in a persession to the par-ish rume, where they zaut down an' rested therzel's, a vew to a taime, 'cuz ther' wadn' nuff cheers to goo round. Then they 'ad a banquit o' blue-vinny chaise, an' pickle cabbidge, supplied be the lan-lord o' the Black 'Oss; wai' zome o' Varmer Urvord's zider wat 'e kips vir the harvesters, to waish it down wai'; or they cude 'ave watter, witchever they prefer. Arter they'd taasted ole Jimmy's zider they all preferred the watter.'

"'CHEWSDY.—The Vrainch Par-ish Coun-cil, conducted by Jan Stewer, paid a visit to the Parish Pump. They all declared 'twas a vurry purty pump, an' aich wan pumpid a vu strauks, jis vir the saake o' bein' abble to zay they 'ad, like. Wan o' the Vrainchies raymarked that if the 'annle 'ad bin a trifle longer, twid a-raich vurder down the zide o' the pump. This raymark was considered very clivver, an' was raysayved wi' loud chairs. Arter theas, ther' was a banquit.

"'WENSDY.—The Vrainch Par-ish Council waint to zee the village clock. Ther' idden no village clock, but they all stude around an' 'ad a gude look to the plaace where the clock ort to be. Wan gen'lman was onder-stude to raymark that if ther' WAS a clock vokes wid aisy be abble to zee wat time 'twaz. This raymark was volleyed by loud chairin'. Then they 'ad a banquit.

"'THURSDY.—The Vrainch Par-ish Coun-cil was all prezented wai' Picter Poas-cards o' the villidge, wai' ' A PRESINT VROM MUDDLECOMBE' wraut all acrass 'em. Arter theas ther' was a banquit.

"'VRIDY.—The Vrainch Par-ish Council was all entertained to a banquit, an' then waint back 'oam in Dick Webber's wagginet. The Muddlecombe Par-ish Council rinned along be'ind so var's Ler'borough Crass zingin', 'Vir they be jolly gude vellers.'"

* * * * * * * *

"Wull, Tom Zalter," says Jim, "yu BE a fule, to zit there an' tull up sitch a string of ole rummidge as that is."

"Wull," says Tom, "an' yu be a double an' tribble fule, to bide there an' harkee to't."

Good Books Come From Devon

Also from Broad Street Publishing

Christopher Tull's books are full of the flavours of the West Country so sit back and enjoy his
funny, moving and thought-provoking stories about life in a rural parish.

In Pastures Green
ISBN 978-0-9557019-0-0

Greener Grows the Grass
ISBN978-0-9557019-1-7

The Green Grass of Summer
ISBN 978-0-9557019-5-5

For Ever in Green Pastures
ISBN978-0-9557019-8-6

Good Honest Beer by Mark Young
Being a personal history of the Midlands brewing giant, Mitchells and Butlers.A well-researched and thoughtful look at the pubs of yesterday and today.
Illustrated with numerous colour and black and white photographs and including a fold-out map of the 90-acre site at Smethwick,Birmingham
ISBN 978-0-9557019-7-9

Available at bookshops
or direct from Broad Street Publishing on 01626 365478

Good Books Come From Devon

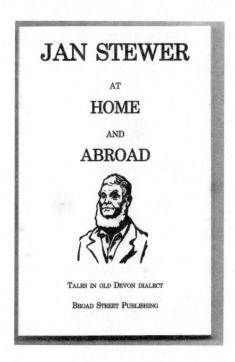